THE ROYAL

A HISTORY OF
» THE ROYAL «
AGRICULTURAL
WINTER FAIR

W. P. WATSON

THE ROYAL

A HISTORY OF
» THE ROYAL «
AGRICULTURAL
WINTER FAIR

MC CLELLAND AND STEWART LIMITED

TORONTO MONTREAL

The Canadian Publishers
McClelland and Stewart Limited
25 Hollinger Road, Toronto 16

Printed and bound in Canada
by McCorquodale & Blades Printers Limited

CONTENTS

Foreword

WHEN the Royal Agricultural Winter Fair was just an idea the Minister and officials of the Ontario Department of Agriculture were among the first to recognize the impact that a national show would have on Canadian agriculture. Their pledges of financial and moral support were important factors in getting the show established. As we, their successors, reflect on developments that have taken place since 1922, one fact stands out: their confidence in the future of the Royal has not been misplaced. We have watched the Royal grow in stature with each passing year and can say in all sincerity that it is truly the show window of Canadian agriculture.

The keen competition generated by this national show has proven to be an inspiration to all who have participated. Although the winners of top awards have derived a great deal of satisfaction from their accomplishments, they were unable to rest on their laurels because, invariably, the less successful competitors were imbued with a spirit of determination to do a better job the following year. In the process they provided an example to others in their respective communities, thus extending the benefits of the competitive system well beyond the confines of the buildings in which the Royal is held. In the final analysis the Royal has made a genuine contribution to improvement in the quality of Canada's livestock and agricultural products and to the development of Canada's export trade in these products.

In view of the fact that the Royal is celebrating its 40th anniversary in 1968, it seems most fitting that a record of the show's development and achievements should be published. The author of this record, W. P. Watson, has been associated with the Royal, either directly or indirectly, since 1922, the year of its birth. In that year he was a member of the Inter-County Live Stock Judging team from Wentworth, his native county. Five years later, while participating in the Inter-College Competition as a member of the team from the Ontario Agricultural College, he won the E. H. Stonehouse trophy, awarded to the contestant winning the highest number of points in judging dairy cattle.

Upon graduating from that institution in 1928 he joined the staff of the Ontario Live Stock Branch where he gained considerable experience in fair management as the result of serving as live stock superintendent of the Western Fair, London, and the Ontario Provincial Winter Fair at Guelph. When, following the War, attempts to revive the Guelph fair failed, Mr. Watson had the unpleasant task of presiding over the liquidation of that organization.

As Live Stock Commissioner, Mr. Watson was responsible for the introduction of many policies that have stood the test of time including artificial insemination and performance testing of beef cattle. He had the distinction of being the first Canadian to serve as chairman of the Board of Directors of Performance Registry International, and was one of the few Canadians to serve on the Board of the International Dairy Show, Chicago. He was one of the founders and the first president of The Canadian Agricultural Hall of Fame Association.

In 1961, Mr. Watson was appointed Assistant Deputy Minister of Agriculture and two years later resigned, after 35 years of service with the Ontario Department of Agriculture, to become General Manager of the Royal Agricultural Winter Fair, the position he now occupies. In 1968, he was made a Fellow of the Agricultural Institute of Canada, the highest honour the Institute can bestow on one of its members.

Thus Mr. Watson's career spans the period of time that the Royal has been operating. Having been a contestant at the first show, a member of many committees including the Executive Committee, he had an excellent opportunity of observing at first hand the many changes and improvements that have taken place. In this book he has described the significant events that took place during the planning stage and in the first 39 years of the Fair's operations. Reference is made to many of the men who played leading roles in elevating the Fair to its present position of prominence in Canadian agriculture. Although the Royal was the creation of a few, the stature which it has attained can be attributed to a pooling of the talents of many. Therefore we are very proud of the fact that the Ontario Department of Agriculture and Food has been an important contributor to and participant in the building of Canada's National Agricultural Fair.

Wm. A. Stewart

MINISTER OF AGRICULTURE AND FOOD,
PROVINCE OF ONTARIO

July 1968

The Royal through the Eyes of the Artist

M. Lowenthal

The Royal Agricultural Winter Fair is a study in contrast — farm animals and hunting pinks; jewels, top hats and rugged herdsmen. Here is fertile ground for the artist, and each year students from the Ontario College of Art are invited to spend a week at the fair. They can sketch or paint whatever catches their eyes. The following delightful portfolio of drawings is selected from work done in 1966 and 1967.

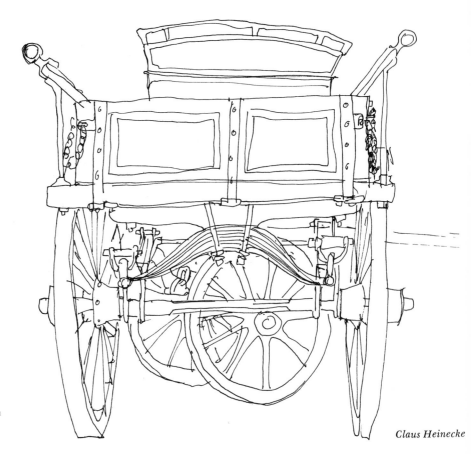

This sturdy wagon
catches an echo
from earlier days

Claus Heinecke

Even a sow needs
her beauty sleep
before she faces
the judges

John Lasruk

Karminski

Competition runs high
in the show ring
as the cattle
are judged

John Lasruk

Brian Smith

Collins

Some artists find
the spectators
more interesting
than the animals

Brian Smith

M. Lowenthal

Vlasta Rabel

The Royal Horse show,
with its colour and
excitement, has done much
to make the Fair
one of the high points
of Toronto's social calendar . . .

ollins

Vlasta Rabel

Fryman

. . . But to the exhibitors,
the Fair's *raison
d'être* is still
the showing
of fine cattle

CHAPTER 1 Early Days

WHEN the first settlers arrived in this country their main concern was to survive. They cut down the trees and built log houses for shelter, then planted seeds in the land that had been cleared to produce their food. After making provision for their sustenance they erected schools, usually of log construction, for the education of their children, and built churches for the edification of their souls.

Their next community project involved the organization of fairs. The first one in Canada was held at Windsor, N.S., in 1765. Twenty-seven years later, in 1792, the first fair in Upper Canada was held at Niagara-on-the-Lake, and established a pattern which was copied in other communities.

The trend towards organizing fairs developed fairly rapidly in the nineteenth century, with the result that these events were being held annually in all sections of Canada by the year 1900. In fact, several fairs were operating in the Northwest Territories before Alberta and Saskatchewan attained provincial status. Thus fairs have the distinction of being the oldest agricultural organizations in this country.

The first fairs bore little resemblance to those of today. Although their central purpose was to display live stock and farm products, the main concern of the settlers was to get enough to eat, so the emphasis was on quantity rather than quality. Under those circumstances, the largest ox and the biggest pumpkin were considered the ultimate in their respective fields.

During the first half of the last century a few of the more progressive farmers began to import pure-bred live stock from

Great Britain, the source of most of the breeds widely distributed in Canada today. As these farmers developed pedigreed herds they acquired the designation 'breeders.' Naturally a friendly spirit of rivalry developed between them, each contending that his animals were better than those of his contemporaries. The two leading questions of the day were which is the best breed, and which are the best animals within each breed. A hundred years have elapsed since these arguments began, and the first question has never been answered although some breeds have become decidedly more popular than others. The second question was decided for the first time about 1850 in the show ring. At this point standards for each breed were established and men familiar with those standards were selected to place the animals paraded before them on the show day in descending order of merit. To facilitate the task of making the selections, animals were divided into classes on the basis of age. This marked the introduction of competition to shows and started a trend under which the emphasis shifted from quantity to quality.

In reflecting on developments of the past century it is of interest to recall that the competitive system, first introduced about 1850, is still a basic feature at all agricultural shows. Admittedly, standards have changed. As a general rule the changes have been motivated by economic considerations, but shows have not attempted to dictate the standards. Invariably these have been established by the breed associations. On the other hand, most fair organizations have striven to provide adequate facilities for showing and to co-operate with breed associations in the selection of judges capable of interpreting the standards to the satisfaction of the exhibitors and spectators.

SELECTING THE SITE FOR THE FAIR

Despite the fact that every province had a well-organized show program by the end of the first decade of the present century, Canada still lacked a national agricultural fair, one that attracted exhibits from every part of the country. Realizing this weakness in our agricultural program, a few men of vision began to advocate the establishment of a fair designed to serve as a show window for Canadian agriculture. Being men of conviction they advanced the idea at every opportunity, but particularly at meetings of live-stock associations and agricultural organizations. Encouraged by the favourable reaction to their submissions, they made representations to the Departments of Agriculture, and were rewarded for their efforts by being assured of support, both financial and otherwise.

Most of the credit for conceiving the idea of a national show and for enlisting the support of the agricultural fraternity should go to W. A. Dryden, the owner of Maple Shade Farm, a well known Shorthorn breeding establishment at Brooklin. Associated with him in his early crusades were George Pepper of Toronto, D. C. Flatt of Millgrove, and Prof. George E. Day of Guelph. These men, working as a committee, formulated most of the plans which resulted in the establishment of the Royal Agricultural Winter Fair.

Fortunately, during the planning stages, they were in a position to draw on the experience of others. The International Live Stock Exposition, founded about the beginning of the century and held annually in Chicago, had many features that could be copied. Held in high repute by live stock breeders on both sides of the border, it attracted exhibitors and spectators from far and wide. At home, the Ontario Provincial Winter Fair, held annually in Guelph, and the Ottawa Winter Fair were making worthwhile contributions to the improvement of live stock in the areas they served. Nevertheless, none of these fairs was operated in conformity with the ideals envisaged by the committee members. Their objective was a fair which would feature competitive classes for all breeds of live stock and varieties of agricultural products produced in this country and which, because of its reputation, would attract the best exhibits from each of the provinces. Furthermore they realized that a show based on exhibits of live stock and agricultural products alone, regardless of how excellent they might be, would not attract the public in large numbers. Consequently their plans included provision for the holding of a horse show.

Their ideas took practical shape with the organization of the National Live Stock and Dairy Show, held in Toronto in 1913. In the following year, Canada became embroiled in World War I and national thought and action were directed in other channels. Late in 1917, when it became apparent that the allied cause would triumph, discussions of a national show were revived. The four pioneer promoters met frequently during the next few months to develop a plan that had promise of receiving general support. When preparatory plans were formulated, a general meeting of leading Ontario live stock breeders was convened in Hamilton under the chairmanship of J. E. Brethour of Burford.

Before the meeting adjourned delegates went on record as supporting the plan in principle. Since it was very elementary indeed, a committee was appointed to work out the details. The members appointed were: William Smith, Columbus, a Clydesdale breeder and importer; J. E. Brethour of Burford, a swine breeder; John Gardhouse of Weston, a Shorthorn breeder; John McKee of Norwich, an Ayrshire breeder; J. D. Brien of Ridgetown, a sheep and swine breeder; William McNeill of London, a poultry breeder and fancier; and W. A. Dryden of Brooklin, a Shorthorn breeder.

These men recognized the need to get the support and cooperation of breed associations. Accordingly, each breed association was invited to name delegates to a meeting, scheduled to be held in the Prince George Hotel, Toronto, on February 22, 1918. After electing Will A. Dryden, chairman, and Prof. George E. Day, secretary, the 48 accredited delegates proceeded to consider the stabling requirements for a national show. Naturally there were differences of opinion among them, but finally they agreed that it would be necessary to provide accommodation for 700 horses, 800 beef cattle, 600 dairy cattle, 1000 sheep, 1000 hogs, and 10,000 poultry. Before the meeting adjourned a sub-committee was appointed to arrange for the drafting of plans for suitable buildings, financing and a site for the fair.

The problem of a site was tackled first. Cities considered to be suitable locations for a national show were given a chance to bid for it. When all proposals were received, the claims of Toronto, Hamilton and London were deemed most worthy of consideration. To reduce the possibility of misunderstanding, members of the committee met with officials of the three cities to explain any issues that might be in doubt. The committee also conferred with officials of the Canadian National Exhibition with a view to using some of the live stock buildings in Exhibition Park. In his presentation to these officials, Mr. Dryden made it abundantly clear that the proposed show would be controlled and managed by representatives of the breed associations and agricultural organizations, and that it would not be operated by the Canadian National Exhibition.

Following this series of meetings the sub-committee recommended that the fair be held in Toronto. When this decision became known several members of the original committee voiced their disapproval in no uncertain terms. To settle the issue a meeting was held in the Royal Connaught Hotel, Hamilton, on October 28, 1919, at which W. A. Dryden presided. In the interval between the announcement that Toronto was being recommended as the site for the fair and the date of the meeting, London's claim was rejected. It was generally agreed that a more central location within the province was preferable. Consequently, when the meeting convened, the choice was between Toronto and Hamilton, with each city having a fairly large number of enthusiastic supporters.

Each of the two cities offered a deal to get the national fair.

Hamilton said it would provide a free site for the buildings and make an annual grant of $20,000 a year for 20 years to help pay for the cost of the buildings, which it estimated would be about $800,000, and would provide free light, heat, power and water. Or, if the fair preferred, Hamilton would offer a straight grant of $250,000.

Toronto said it would provide a site on the Exhibition Grounds and put up a $1,000,000 building. The fair would pay back to the city $40,000 a year for 10 years, and another $10,000 a year over the same period as rental. In effect, the fair would pay back half the city's $1,000,000 investment in the building. Not to be outdone, Toronto would also throw in free light, heat, power and water.

Both these offers, however, were contingent on the fair obtaining about $50,000 in grants from the provincial and federal governments for prize money, and raising another $50,000 on its own.

Although not a voting delegate, Controller Sam McBride, one of the most colourful figures at Toronto's City Hall, made an eloquent plea in which he pointed out the many advantages to be gained from locating the fair in the Queen City. His arguments were countered with equal vigour and sincerity by representatives of the Hamilton Council. When the chairman called for action, J. E. Brethour moved and Alex Hume, an Ayrshire breeder from Campbellford, seconded a motion to the effect that the fair be located in Hamilton. Immediately thereafter, J. M. Gardhouse of Weston and D. O. Bull of Brampton, two men who were destined to play important roles in the affairs of the show, moved and seconded that it be located in Toronto. Excitement was intense as the ballots were passed to the official delegates and reached a climax when the results were announced: 18 votes for Hamilton, 18 votes for Toronto. Thus, the issue was placed squarely on the shoulders of Mr. Dryden, as chairman, who cast the deciding ballot in favour of Toronto. Consequently, the man who had envisioned a national agricultural show also had the distinction of determining its location.

ROYAL, A TRULY NATIONAL SHOW

Before the first fair was held, the founders were assured of the moral support and good wishes of the leading agricultural organizations in Canada. In turn, they requested that the good wishes be backed by financial contributions to convert the vision into a reality. Governments and other interested parties acceded to these requirements by pledging enough support to underwrite the prizes. The governments of Canada and Ontario were the first to respond. They each agreed to make grants of $25,000 annually for a period of ten years. Their lead was followed by breed associations, most of whom offered to make annual grants to be used in supplementing the prizes offered for their particular breeds.

One of the first to commit support from business was Frank C. Fletcher, manager of the Union Stock Yards Company, who pledged $2,500 a year for ten years. Mr. Fletcher was a devoted supporter from the outset and always prized his connection with the Royal. He was universally admired as a gentleman and a "straight-shooter," and served on the Executive Committee continuously from 1922 to 1963. He served as vice president in 1938, but never became president.

Other pledges of $1,000 a year for a 10-year period were received from Swift Canadian Co., William Davies Co., Gunns Ltd., Sir John Eaton, H. C. Cox, Alfred Rogers, the County of York, and the Dominion Express Co.

At the end of the ten-year period, these financial subscribers did not renew their undertakings. At this point, however, several provinces – Alberta, Saskatchewan, Quebec, New Brunswick, Nova Scotia and Prince Edward Island – began to make annual grants in amounts varying from $250 to $5,000. While these grants may seem small compared with those made by the federal and Ontario governments, they represent only a portion of the total contribution of these provinces towards the Royal.

To ensure the national character of the show, the governments of all provinces, except Ontario, entered into agreements with the federal government under which exhibitors would be reimbursed for transportation and certain other costs incurred in exhibiting at the Royal. In each case, responsibility for administering the policy was assumed by the provincial government and most provincial governments appointed committees to inspect prospective entries and to select such animals as appeared to be potential prize winners. As the result of adopting this policy, each province is represented at the Royal by the best animals available. Although assistance of a similar nature is available on farm products, control over entries is not exercised to the same degree. In any event the financial support rendered by the provinces is substantially greater, and of more significance to the Royal, than that made in the form of outright grants.

When the first Royal was held, more than half the pure bred live stock breeders of Canada lived in Ontario. Throughout the war years and for a few years thereafter, Western farmers experienced a period of unprecedented prosperity. Wheat crops were good, markets were readily available and prices were at record levels. Except for the ranching areas of Alberta, there was little interest in live stock production. Within a decade the situation changed; wheat markets vanished, prices plunged to less than 50 cents per bushel at Fort William and many Western wheat growers became destitute. In their hour of adversity the Western farmers turned to live stock production. As the number of commercial herds and flocks increased the pure bred industry expanded. Within a few years the number of breeders of pure bred cattle, sheep and swine in Western Canada exceeded that of Ontario.

Today, Canadian live stock enjoys an enviable reputation throughout the world. That reputation is based on the fact that it has a high rating from the standpoint of type, production and health. Every show in this country has contributed to the improvement in type that has taken place. Until the Royal was established, however, much of that contribution was ineffective. With the opening of a national show the stage was set for bringing together the best animals from all parts of Canada. Thus, it became possible to establish national type standards, standards that could be copied at all other shows.

Undoubtedly the adoption of policies designed to assist exhibitors from other provinces in showing at the Royal has been an important factor in maintaining the Royal's status as Canada's national show. Nevertheless these offers of support would not have produced the results that have been achieved if the men responsible for making them had failed to visualize the benefits that would accrue from participating in a national show. Among those who had faith in the Royal and who strongly supported it in their respective provinces were: Jim Bell, Live Stock Commissioner and later Deputy Minister of Agriculture for Manitoba; J. G. Robertson, Live Stock Commissioner for Saskatchewan; Stanley Longman, Deputy Minister of Agriculture for Alberta; Adrien Morin, Live Stock Commissioner for Quebec; J. K. King and Waldo Walsh, Deputy Minister of Agriculture for New Brunswick and Nova Scotia respectively, and Walter Shaw, Deputy Minister of Agriculture and later Premier of Prince Edward Island.

The leading proponents of the Royal in the federal field were Dr. J. H. Grisdale, Deputy Minister of Agriculture, and H. S. Arkell, Live Stock Commissioner. Both took an active part in the discussions at the early committee meetings and were largely responsible for shaping the policies under which financial assistance was made available to the Royal and to exhibitors at the Royal.

Of course, officials of the Ontario Department of Agriculture have always been proud of the fact that the Royal was located in their province. Hence, from the outset their support has been more or less automatic. Nevertheless, special mention should be made of the support given by the Hon. Manning Doherty, Minister of Agriculture at the time the Royal was being organized; W. B. Roadhouse, the Deputy Minister, and R. W. Wade, the Live Stock Commissioner.

These men, along with the leading live stock breeders and agriculturists in their respective provinces, were strong advocates of a national show and leaders in enlisting provincial support for the Royal. They were able to impress upon their associates the importance of the cause. Due to their leadership, their successors are promoting the welfare of the Royal with equal vigour.

FIRST ROYAL HELD IN 1922

Undoubtedly the next three years (1920-22) were the most difficult in the history of the new organization. There were many frustrations and some recriminations before success was finally achieved. Having disposed of the controversial issue of selecting a location for the fair, steps were taken to obtain a charter from the Ontario government. The committee decided to incorporate under the name, "The Agricultural Winter Fair Association of

Canada." Letters patent, duly granted on November 24, 1919, list the following Ontario gentlemen as signers to the application and charter members of the Association:

W. A. Dryden, Brooklin; H. C. Cox, Oakville; J. J. Morrison, Toronto; O. W. Waller, Toronto; Harry McGee, Toronto; Harry M. Robinson, Toronto; C. F. Bailey, Toronto; Alfred Rogers, Toronto; William Inglis, Toronto; George Pepper, Toronto; Hon. George S. Henry, Todmorden; L. O. Clifford, M.P., Oshawa; J. D. Brien, Ridgetown; W. W. Ballantyne, Stratford; E. C. H. Tisdale, Beaverton; J. M. Gardhouse, Weston; E. H. Stonehouse, Weston; H. D. Smith, Ancaster; John McKee, Norwich; J. H. Saunders, London; Lt. Col. Robert E. McEwen, London; J. E. Brethour, Burford; George E. Day, Guelph; Harry M. Pettit, Burlington; D. O. Bull, Brampton, and William Smith, Columbia.

A general meeting of the new organization was held in the Prince George Hotel on November 24, 1919 to elect the first slate of officers. Those elected at that meeting were: President, W. A. Dryden; Vice-President, H. C. Cox; Executive Committee: O. W. Waller, Harry McGee, W. W. Ballantyne, J. J. Morrison, George Pepper, and Prof. George E. Day.

Prof. Day was named Treasurer of the Association and the Executive Committee was authorized to engage Mr. C. F. Bailey of the Ontario Department of Agriculture, as Managing-Director. These instructions were carried out promptly and Mr. Bailey began his new duties on January 22, 1920.

In the meantime, some of the directors began to have reservations about the name of the organization, feeling that it should be given a more distinctive title, particularly one that included the word "Royal." In due course, an application for a change in title was made through the proper channels to His Majesty, King George V, who graciously granted this request. Accordingly, letters patent were issued on March 22, 1920, under which the organization, by virtue of the highest authority in the Empire, was officially designated "The Royal Agricultural Winter Fair Association of Canada."

Early in the same year a committee under the chairmanship of George Pepper was appointed to draft plans for the buildings, and the financing of them. Being a dedicated but somewhat dogmatic person, Mr. Pepper devoted his entire time and energy to the task, but in the process was guilty of failing to consult other members of the committee. However he did work closely with the city architect in designing the plans and with city treasury officials in developing the financial arrangements.

In view of the fact that the buildings were of concern to the Canadian National Exhibition and the city, as well as to the Royal, the original plans were changed several times. Under the arrangement finally approved, the city undertook to erect an arena capable of seating 7,500 people and the annexes adjacent thereto at an estimated cost of one million dollars. In return, the Royal agreed to reimburse the city at the rate of $40,000 per year for ten years and to pay an annual rental of $10,000.

The directors of the Royal were quite confident they could carry out this commitment. After all, the federal and Ontario governments had promised annual grants of $25,000 each. Business concerns and private individuals had pledged generous financial support for the next decade. In addition, breed associations had given assurances of substantial grants in aid of prize money. Consequently the agreement was signed and construction started in May of 1921.

It was generally understood that the building would be completed in time for the holding of a show in late November, 1921, and the directors proceeded on that assumption. Prize lists were printed, exhibit space was rented and the 1921 fair was widely advertised. But, early in October, it became apparent that the building would not be ready for occupancy. Although the construction might be completed, there was no possibility of the heating system being ready for operation. Therefore, on October 20, the President, after consultation with his directors and Mayor T. L. Church, reluctantly announced that the 1921 Royal was being cancelled.

In addition to the disappointment experienced by many, cancellation of the 1921 show resulted in a heavy financial loss to the Association and the directors were obliged to review their financial position. In doing so, it became apparent that they would never be able to carry out their agreement with the city. Even the most optimistic directors realized that annual payments of $50,000 were more than the Royal would ever be able to pay.

Differences of opinion regarding ways of coping with the situation developed among the directors. Generally speaking, they were divided into two groups: one contending that to reduce operating costs, management of the Royal should be vested in the Canadian National Exhibition; the other declaring that such action would constitute a betrayal of the principles upon which the Association was established. George Pepper was the leader of the group that favoured transferring control to the Canadian National Exhibition, while C. F. Bailey became identified with the opposing group. Bad feelings developed and the situation became intolerable to Bailey. As a result he tendered his resignation as managing director in March of 1922. Even with Bailey out of the picture, Pepper was unable to rally a majority of the directors to support his cause, so he resigned a few weeks later.

At this point Alexander P. Westervelt, who had been serving on the staff in a junior capacity, was appointed managing director. Mr. Westervelt was a man of wide experience, having served as manager of the Ontario Provincial Winter Fair, at Guelph, director of the Ontario Live Stock Branch, and at the time of his employment as a member of the Federal Department of Agriculture. While his appointment was strongly supported, a few members of the Board still contended that the interests of the fair could be best served under c.n.e. management. Because this sentiment prevailed, a committee was appointed to discuss the matter with Mr. Kent, the c.n.e. manager. During the interview he stated quite emphatically that in his opinion it would be unwise to integrate the operations of the two fairs.

With Mr. Westervelt firmly in the saddle and the issue with respect to integration resolved, the directors proceeded to negotiate a new agreement with the city and to make plans for the 1922 fair. In all of these negotiations, the directors and management were guided by the advice of Mr. Peter White, k.c., a prominent Toronto lawyer, who served as legal advisor to the Royal until the time of his death. After a great deal of discussion, the city agreed to cancel the original agreement and to enter into a new one under which the Royal was obliged to pay to the city, annually, all profits in excess of $10,000.

The success of the first Royal Agricultural Winter Fair surprised even the visionary optimists who had conceived it. In fact, it almost lived up to the extravagant advertising and circus-type press-agentry which preceded it.

Advertisements in the Toronto newspapers had promised that the still-unborn Royal would "Reveal the Marvels of a Winter Exposition Unprecedented in the History of Any Nation in the world!"

Among the enticements offered were a "Horse Show Extraordinary," "California Frank's Mammoth Western Circus," a

"Modern Indoor Midway" with "Amusement Features Galore,"
"The World's Greatest Display of Livestock" and – to top it all
off – "J. Wilson Jardine's Augmented Symphony Orchestra."

On Monday November 20, two days before the opening of
the show, more than 200 freight cars of live stock were delivered
to the grounds via the Grand Trunk and Canadian Pacific Railways. There were 25 carloads of cattle from the U.S.

C. Alfred Maguire, Mayor of Toronto, issued a proclamation
urging the good citizens of Toronto to turn out and support this
precedent-shattering extravaganza, adding: "It is also requested
that citizens display decorations at their residences and places of
business in honour of the occasion."

There was a brisk trade in general admission tickets at 25
cents, and children were admitted on opening day for a nickel.
It cost you another quarter to get into the horse show ring, or 50
cents, 75 cents or $1.25 for a reserved seat.If you were a member
of the affluent upper-crust you could take a box at the horse show
for the week at $40 for a four-seat box or $50 for a six-seat box.

The Grand Trunk was bringing three passenger trains a day
direct to the grounds from "Hamilton, Brantford, Woodstock,
London and beyond." Two hundred people arrived on a special
train from Prince Edward Island.

As a special bargain, you could buy a strip of five admission
tickets for a dollar and save yourself 25 cents. The management
warned, however, that the supply of bargain tickets was "about
exhausted" and urged the public to "get busy and fortify yourself
with one which may be obtained at all leading hotels, cigar
stores, railway ticket offices, druggists and news dealers."
Strangely enough, the supply of bargain tickets, which was
threatened with exhaustion a week before the fair began, was
still adequate for the demand on closing day.

During the last week in November 1922, the Royal was run-
ning against some pretty stiff competition for the attention of
Toronto citizens. Rudolph Valentino was playing in "The
Young Rajah" at Shea's Hippodrome. Jackie Cooper in
"Trouble" was playing at the Pantages Theatre. Lionel Barry-
more was at Loew's in "The Face in the Fog." If your taste was
more high-class you could go to hear Rachmaninoff, "Famous
Russian Pianist," at Massey Hall.

Instead of buying a dollar strip of bargain tickets to the
Royal, for the same price you could enjoy a real old-fashioned,
full course Thanksgiving dinner at the Walker House or the

Carls-Rite Hotel. Or, for 75 cents, you could buy yourself one of the latest hit records – "Toot, toot tootsie Good Bye!" or Al Jolson singing "I Wish I Could Shimmy Like My Sister Kate" – and stay home and play it on your new-fangled gramaphone.

Nevertheless, about 22,000 Torontonians and their country cousins passed up these seductive attractions on opening day and decided instead to come to the Royal and have a look for themselves at "The Peer of Indoor Expositions."

When the box office opened for the first time at 8.00 A.M. on Wednesday, November 22, 1922, it was cloudy and a few degrees below freezing. The city had the first light snow fall of the year but it was all gone well before noon. The first people to buy a ticket were E. A. Haines and his wife, who had come from their farm six miles west of Parry Sound.

"I haven't been in Toronto in ten years," Mr. Haines explained, "so we thought we would take a holiday and see this show."

The Haines were followed by enthusiastic crowds, estimated at more than 150,000, who arrived all week by street-cars, which were just in the process of being transferred from the old Toronto Street Railway to the new Toronto Transportation Commission, by Grand Trunk and CPR trains, and in a procession of somewhat primitive Fords, Maxwells, Packards, Studebakers, Durants and Peerless Eights.

In the week that followed the Royal distributed $70,000 in prize money among exhibitors from every province in Canada and nine states in the U.S. who showed 17,000 entries, including 1,850 horses, 2,500 cattle, 900 sheep, 700 swine and 9,100 poultry.

When it was all over, the Toronto *Globe* announced the "popular verdict" in the headline:

ROYAL WINTER FAIR
GREATEST ON EARTH

The Toronto *Star* was a little more cautious:

THE BEST AND BIGGEST OF ITS KIND
ON THE CONTINENT OF AMERICA
IF NOT IN ALL THE WORLD

"In one day," the *Globe* reported, "the expenditure of more than a million dollars on the huge Coliseum was justified. In 12 hours an international show second to none in the world came into being. It was a triumph for Toronto, for the Province and for the Dominion."

THE BUILDING PROGRAM
At the first Royal the arena was used for judging live stock and staging the horse show. Farm products and poultry were displayed in the annexes. The live stock were housed in about 30 different structures including frame stables along the railway tracks, immediately north of the arena. From the standpoint of comfort these stables were adequate at the time of the Canadian National Exhibition, but during the cold and sometimes wet days of November they left much to be desired. In fact, on many occasions the passages in the stables resembled the beds of small streams, while the area between the stables and the arena was often a sea of mud.

Matt Aikman, the Royal's office manager, who was an office boy at the time of the first show, recalls that he had to keep a pair of rubber boots beside his desk and put them on whenever he was required to make the treacherous crossing to deliver messages in the stables.

In fact, the only dissenting voice in the chorus of praise for the first Royal was concerned with accommodation – for beasts and men.

A reporter for the Toronto *Star* commented:

"The accommodation this year proved woefully insufficient for the enormous entries of live stock. Some fine cattle were standing in water part of the time. Cattle had to be kept in open runways between buildings. At least two men who slept in the stable with their stock have contacted pneumonia from the bad weather conditions."

Despite the unsatisfactory stabling conditions, entries continued to increase. Soon it became apparent to all concerned that the live stock exhibited at Canada's national agricultural show were worthy of larger and better accommodation. Accordingly approaches were made to the governments of Canada and Ontario. Being fully appreciative of the role played by the Royal in the development of Canadian agriculture, they agreed to finance the cost of buildings to house cattle, sheep and swine. Work on the buildings began in 1926 and was completed in time for the 1927 show, thereby providing excellent accommodation for approximately 2,000 cattle, 1,200 sheep and 1,000 swine. The cost of these buildings, amounting to $1,400,000 was shared equally by the federal and Ontario governments.

With the completion of these buildings adequate facilities were available for all classes of live stock except horses. Their requirements were met in 1931 by the construction of the Horse Palace. This project, estimated to cost $900,000, was undertaken during the depression, partly as a means of relieving unemployment. The cost was to be shared equally by the governments of Canada, Ontario, and the City of Toronto. The federal share was paid during a three-year period, whereas the commitments of the other two governments were amortized over 20 years. When interest charges were added, their total payments amount to considerably more than that of the federal government.

Although the governments of Canada and Ontario contributed more than 60 per cent of the total cost of the buildings, ownership was vested in the City of Toronto. In accepting this gift the city agreed to assume responsibility for their maintenance, to make the buildings available, rent free, to the Royal for such time as might be necessary for staging a fair annually, and to a number of other terms and conditions. On the other hand, the buildings were to be used for the agricultural division of the Canadian National Exhibition, and the city was granted the right to rent them for other purposes when not being used by the Royal or the Exhibition. Actually these buildings were used for little else until 1939.

When Canada entered the war in September of that year buildings that could be converted into barracks were commandeered by the military. Among the first to be requisitioned were the Coliseum and its adjacent buildings. Thousands of troops were stationed there between 1939 and 1945 and, of course, the Royal was cancelled during that period.

This turn of events caused a great deal of disappointment to the dozens of commercial producers who had fitted animals in anticipation of showing them at the 1939 Royal. However, Frank Fletcher stepped into the breach by offering the facilities of the Union Stock Yards for the holding of a special show and sale of market live stock. This event was managed by the staff of the Ontario Live Stock Branch. Similar shows were held in the two years following, but were discontinued when meat rationing and price ceilings were introduced.

Following the cessation of hostilities the buildings were returned to their owner and plans were made for resuming the

Royal. The first post-war show, held in 1946, attracted record crowds. In fact, on Saturday afternoon, the buildings were filled to capacity and hundreds who were clamouring to get in had to be turned away.

The experience of the war years demonstrated that the buildings could be used for something else besides staging agricultural shows. One of the first to exploit this possibility was the Department of Trade and Commerce. Fearing a recession, such as occurred after the first World War, the Department organized an International Trade Show which operated for two weeks for several consecutive years. This proved to be very successful, so much so that other trade or industry shows were organized to stimulate business within the country. The number of such shows continued to increase and as a result the building used to house cattle at the Royal was renamed the Industry Building.

Entries at the Royal continued to increase too, and as they did it became necessary to erect temporary pens to house sheep and swine, to tie cattle closer together than they should be tied, and to delay the time of arrival of some of the horses entered in the line classes until others could be judged and sent home. In addition, many of the facilities had become completely outmoded. Consequently an appeal was made to the governments that had contributed to the cost of the original buildings. In 1949, Col. T. L. Kennedy, the acting Premier of Ontario, announced that his government would make a grant of one million dollars towards the cost of enlarging and remodelling the facilities used for staging the Royal, on condition that similar amounts were contributed by the Government of Canada and the City of Toronto. Shortly thereafter Hiram E. McCallum, Mayor of Toronto, gave an undertaking that the city would match this offer, and three years later the Government of Canada did likewise.

A building committee under the chairmanship of Stewart G. Bennett was set up to formulate plans. Unfortunately the members could not agree. Some wanted money used to erect additional judging facilities, while others showed a preference for more stabling accommodation for live stock. Despite the fact that the offer was made for the purpose of improving facilities for the Royal, c.n.e. officials felt that they should be involved on the grounds that they were acting as agents for the city in matters pertaining to the operations of the buildings.

Eventually the original committee was disbanded and a joint C.N.E. – Royal Winter Fair committee was named under the chairmanship of J. A. Northey, a man who had served as president of both shows. Although this committee tried diligently to resolve the differences of opinion, they failed and the committee became inactive. For a few years it appeared that the project might be dropped. Finally in 1959, Hon. W. A. Goodfellow, Minister of Agriculture for Ontario, convened a meeting of a small group representing the city, the Province, the C.N.E., and the Royal, and announced that the offer would be withdrawn unless action was taken immediately. Following that meeting, another committee was named, comprised of: George Bell, Commissioner of Parks and Recreation, representing the city; W. P. Watson, Live Stock Commissioner for Ontario, representing the Ontario government; W. S. McMullen, senior officer of the Canada Department of Agriculture in Ontario, representing the federal government; H. E. McCallum, General Manager of the C.N.E., and J. H. Crang, President of the Royal Agricultural Winter Fair. In the following year George Rodanz, the newly elected President of the Royal, replaced Mr. Crang on the committee.

This committee met on several occasions and reviewed the requirements, keeping in mind that the buildings were likely to be used by several organizations. In reaching decisions, however, the needs of the Royal were given top priority. Work began immediately following the 1960 fair. The original sheep building was demolished and replaced by a two-storey sheep and swine building, with each floor providing accommodation for approximately 1,000 head of sheep or swine. Provision was made for using portable pens which could be removed and stored in the event that the building was needed for other purposes. Pens were removed from the original swine barn, the floors were levelled and portable stanchions were installed, thus creating a valuable addition to the cattle barn by providing stabling for another 400 head. Provision was made for penning entries in the group classes for steers in this building, a major improvement since the carlots of steers had been penned in outside pens in previous years.

In the following year, a new milk house was constructed and equipped with modern facilities for handling the milk produced during the C.N.E. and Royal. The main arena was renovated by removing all steel posts supporting the roof, except the four in the corners, thus providing most of the spectators with an unobstructed view of proceedings in the ring. The narrow wooden chairs in the reserved seat area were removed and replaced by wider, tilt-bottomed seats. As a result of replacing narrow seats with wider ones, the seating capacity was reduced about 1,000.

The final major project involved the construction of a new front on the Coliseum. This not only improved the external appearance of the building but provided a large foyer, complete with fountain and a gallery for hanging the portraits of persons named to the Canadian Agricultural Hall of Fame.

While plans for these projects were being formulated, a herdsmen's dormitory was erected, largely with funds supplied by the federal government. This has proven to be a source of great satisfaction to the exhibitors, in that it provides them with comfortable sleeping facilities on the grounds. As the result of improvements made during the past 10-12 years, the Royal has one of the finest sets of agricultural buildings in the world.

MILESTONES

The dates of the first Royal Agricultural Winter Fair – Wednesday, November 22 to Wednesday, November 29, 1922 – were chosen to accommodate exhibitors who wanted to show at the Chicago International and the Ontario Provincial Winter Fair in Guelph. Under this schedule exhibitors could show at the Royal, move on to Chicago and return to Guelph for the wind-up of the show season. They were allowed to keep their animals for several days in the Toronto buildings until it was time to ship them to Guelph.

The first show was so successful that the directors decided to extend the period by one day the following year. Although it has frequently been suggested that the period should be further extended, the Royal has remained an eight-day show since 1923.

In 1925 the Chicago directors, after consultation with Royal officials, decided to advance the dates of their show, with the starting date to be the day following the U.S. Thanksgiving, that is the last Thursday in November. As a result, the Royal closed on the U.S. Thanksgiving Day, an arrangement which proved objectionable to U.S. exhibitors who had problems crossing the border on a holiday. Consequently, in 1936 and continuing through 1951, the Royal opened on a Tuesday and closed on a Wednesday.

During this period it became obvious that the attendance was much higher on Friday and Saturday than on other days. In the hope of capitalizing on this situation, a change was made in 1952, and the fair opened on a Friday and closed on the Saturday of the following week. Since then the largest crowds have attended on the two Saturdays of the fair.

A rather significant event took place in 1965 with the holding of the first Sunday Horse Show. The directors had considered the possibility of opening the entire show on Sunday, but commercial exhibitors were not anxious to operate their booths on that day. Furthermore provincial laws prohibited the operation of shows of any kind on Sundays before 1:30 in the afternoon. Because of the objections and prohibitions, activities in the buildings were restricted to Horse Show matinee performances and they proved very popular with Toronto audiences. In 1968, the law was further liberalized to permit the full operation of agricultural shows on Sundays.

In 1934, to commemorate the 100th anniversary of the incorporation of the City of Toronto, the Royal established a Roll of Honour, paying tribute to every exhibitor awarded a first prize at the show held that year. An individual Diploma of Honour was presented to each person whose name was inscribed on the Roll.

In 1947, arrangements were made for producing a 30-minute film of the Royal, with the costs underwritten by the Imperial Leaf Tobacco Company of Canada Limited. Scenes were filmed in all divisions of the 1947 show. A great many prints were produced and these were made available through the offices of the National Film Board throughout Canada and many countries of the world. Undoubtedly this film did much to advertise the Royal, particularly in foreign countries. Because of the frequency with which they were shown, the films became shop-worn within ten years.

A new film was produced at the 1967 fair under the sponsorship of Massey-Ferguson Industries Limited. The sound track was recorded in English, French and Spanish, in the interest of world-wide distribution.

The first Royal was officially opened by His Honour Col. Henry Cockshutt, Lieutenant Governor of Ontario. In the years following, the Royal has been honoured by having men prominent in the public life of Canada and other countries officiate at the opening ceremonies. H.R.H., The Prince Philip, Duke of

Edinburgh, K.G., opened the fair in 1967, Canada's Centennial Year.

Although the objects of the Royal are stated in the constitution, they were outlined much more precisely in the program of 1922. The announcement reads as follows:

The objects of the Royal Agricultural Winter Fair are:

1. To establish in Canada a National and International Exposition commensurate with the progress and development of Canadian agriculture;
2. To bring together into one big National Winter Fair the best that Canada produces in live stock and poultry, in dairy products, in fruit products, and horticultural display, in vegetables, in seed grain and in production of all kinds from the land;
3. To bring to the attention of the peoples of this and other countries the high quality and excellence of the farms of Canada, with the object of widening the market and increasing the value of such products.

Has the Royal succeeded in carrying out these objectives? Perhaps the answer will be found in the chapters following, each of which deals with developments in a particular division of the fair.

HORSE SHOW

Early Canadian Team rider Lt. Col. Charles Baker

Canadian Military Team Captain, Squadron Leader Douglas J. Cleland on "Chamoro," 1948

Members of inter-
national teams are
welcomed at Toronto
City Hall by Controller
David Balfour

Mounties parade through
downtown streets,
opening day, 1949

Jim Day ties record
height of 7'3" at 1967
International Jumping
Competition

Moffat Dunlap on
"Lights Out"

Gail Ross on
"The Hood"

Tom Gayford, Moffat
Dunlap, Gail Ross and
Jim Day win the
International Trophy
in 1966 for the first
time in 20 years

A six-horse Percheron
team

Herb Coad and Tom
Gayford, on the retire-
ment of "Blue Beau"

Competing for the
Roadster Champion-
ship

"King Clancy" retires –
here seen with his
namesake, King Clancy,
and J. Lance Rumble

A team of Hackneys

Dressage Exhibition by
Christilot Hanson

Coaching Class team
driven by Mrs. Hayden,
famous English whip

The Lipizzan Stallions from the Spanish Riding School in Vienna

Special guest Arthur Godfrey on his horse, "Goldie"

Lt. Col. Clifford Sifton, long-time member of the Horse Show Committee

"Arnprior Emigrant," a famous Clydesdale champion, 1927

Opening night of the
first Horse Show, 1922

Herdsmen relax after
the show with a
sing-song in the
horse barn

CHAPTER 2 Horse Show

TO many people, particularly those who live in the city, the Royal means the Horse Show, and, while this attitude sometimes creates some resentment on the part of those whose main interest in the fair is showing – or looking at – livestock and farm products, the fact is that the fair could probably never have survived financially if it had not been for the glamour and excitement that surrounds fine horses.

The Royal Horse Show, on its very first night, achieved an atmosphere of excellence which it has maintained and enhanced ever since.

Here is how one Toronto *Star* reporter saw the scene on Wednesday November 22, 1922:

Toronto was utterly unprepared for the beauty, the style, the sophistication of this show . . .

It discovered a new side to Toronto. Toronto is getting to be a big girl now. She came out last night with her hair done up and wearing a gown. New York stuff. Metropolitan stuff. What they call 'haut mond.'

The roof was hidden in shadowy buntings, yellow, blue and red. Great lights hung down casting soft light in the ring. The ring was carpeted with dull red tan bark and surrounded with a white fence . . . Off in a corner, an orchestra – not a band – played opera tunes. There were more silk hats in the great crowd than Toronto ever dreamed it owned . . . There were gowns that are never seen except at private functions, and pails and pails of jewels.

As always, on the women's pages of the newspapers, there was more concern with the beauty in the boxes than in the tanbark ring. The *Telegram's* "Woman About Town" gave her readers this breathless, horse's-eye view of the arena:

Women's costumes struck a gayer note at last night's horse show. Vivid hats with much ostrich plumage were seen in the boxes and along the promenade. Jade green held its own, and among the henna family hats was a lovely velvet model in the duller wallflower shade, worn with a frock to match and mole coat, while huge topaz drop earrings encircled with diamonds also reflected the season's vogue for yellow tones. Flowers, too, were seen on some of the smartest hats and one of the most effective costumes was an amethyst duvetyn worn with a big hat in a new reddish purple shade of velvet softly draped and finished with a huge flat velvet rose that almost covered the crown. Many of the women in the boxes wore evening gowns without hats, and it was noticed many men in evening dress defied the silk topper and donned soft felt hats and cozy fur coats.

Nevertheless, ostrich plumage and topaz-and-diamond earrings notwithstanding, it was the horses that created the horse show and the Royal, held during the interval between the National Horse Show in New York and the International Livestock Exposition and Horse Show in Chicago, attracted many of the best animals entered at one or both of these shows.

Within a few years, during which time the Royal established an enviable reputation as one of the finest shows on the continent, it became traditional for the leading U.S. stables to compete in Toronto. Important as these U.S. entries have been, however, the real strength of the show stems from the solid support it has received from Canadian horsemen. From the very outset every true lover of horse flesh has been imbued with an inherent desire to own a horse good enough to show at the Royal.

In the early years it was customary to judge live stock every forenoon and from 1:00 to 3:00 o'clock in the afternoons. Thus the arena was available for staging horse shows in the late afternoons and evenings. Indeed that was all the time needed since there were only 79 classes at the first show. In the years following and particularly during the post-war years many new classes and, in some cases, entire divisions, were added. By 1966 the total number of classes was about double that of 1922, and the time allotted for judging had increased accordingly.

At the first show there were classes for Roadsters, Harness horses, Harness ponies, Saddle horses, Hunters, Jumpers, Polo ponies, Remounts, commercial horses and six-horse, heavy draught teams. Because the horse, in those days, was not only the hobby of country gentlemen, but was still an important form of transportation, Roadsters, Harness horses and commercial horses shared the spotlight. If you are old enough to remember 1922 – when the baker, the milkman, the iceman, the junkman, and the man calling "kindling w-o-o-o-d!" – all came with a horse and wagon, you will know why the Royal staged "commercial classes." Separate classes were provided for bakers and confectioners, butchers, dairymen, express companies, ice cream companies and coal companies, all of which used horses almost exclusively for delivery purposes. These classes were continued until 1938, but were dropped following the war, when trucks began to drive the baker's wagon from the streets.

International Jumping Competitions have always been popular at the Royal, hinting, as they do, at memories of gallant cavalry charges and rallying bugle calls. In fact, in 1922, and for many years thereafter, participation in these classes was restricted to military personnel. In the stiff military dignity of the day, there were classes for officers and separate classes for non-commissioned officers. In each case, however, competition was open to all nations and all branches of the military. In 1925, the classifications was broadened to include team classes, with each team to be comprised of three members of the armed forces, and the G. Howard Ferguson trophy, donated by the Premier of Ontario, became available for perpetual competition. The first year it was offered, teams from Belgium, France, the United States and Canada competed, Belgium won. The Canadian team that year was Major R. S. Timmis, Captain Stuart C. Bate and Lieutenant G. F. Elliott. (A list of the trophy winners in subsequent years and the names of the Canadian riders appear in the Appendix.)

In the next decade, all teams, other than those representing the United States and Canada, came from Europe. During that ten-year span Belgium, Czechoslovakia, France, Germany, Great Britain, Holland, Hungary, Irish Free State and Sweden were represented in the competition. In 1935, Chile became the first Latin American country to participate. Since then teams from Argentina, Brazil, Cuba, Mexico and Peru have competed.

The Royal Horse Show followed the tradition of the Old Toronto Horse Show that was held annually in the Armouries, up until the outbreak of war in 1914, and it has always had a military flavour. In the years before World War II, the Royal Canadian Dragoons occupied barracks close to the Coliseum and the officers' mess and the ballroom were frequently the scene of some of the horse show's less inhibited, informal celebrations.

After World War II, however, when the officer's mount was relegated to ceremonial occasions, the ranks of the jumping classes were filled out by civilians and most governments ceased to assume responsibility for sending teams abroad. Those interested in the sport had to devise ways and means of financing the teams.

On several occasions substantial sums of money were raised privately by members of the Horse Show Administrative Committee in order to maintain a Canadian team. Later on this essential function was taken over by the Canadian Equestrian Association which was organized for the purpose. Due to these efforts, the dedication and sacrifice on the part of team members, and the generosity of owners who lent horses, Canada has continued to participate in international events.

Even before the critical stage developed, industry was making generous contributions in support of international competition. Among the firms making large donations at various times were Joseph E. Seagram and Company, McColl-Frontenac Oil Company, Canadian Oil Company, Shell Oil Company, O'Keefe Brewing Company and Ford Motor Company. In most cases their gifts were used to pay a portion of the cost of bringing competing teams to Toronto.

The Royal never had a monopoly on International Jumping events. In the pre-war years teams competed at New York before coming to Toronto. Since the war Harrisburg and occasionally Washington have been added to the circuit. The living and travelling expenses of the riders, grooms, and horses are shared equally by the shows at which they participate during the time they are on the circuit.

Although International Jumping classes have received the greatest amount of publicity and acclaim, each event in the Horse Show has its devoted following of enthusiasts and experts,

54

and the Royal has always tried to keep in step with the trends. Some of the most popular classes are those for three and five gaited saddle horses; coach horses, hitched to splendid turnouts from the last century; Arabians, paraded by riders attired in native costumes; Palominos with silver mounted saddles and bridles which, in some cases, are more valuable than the horses; and Quarter Horses, the favourite saddle horses of ranchers all over North America. The Green Meadows Coaching Class, for elegant turn-of-the-century coaches shown with a four-horse hitch, were introduced in 1964, thanks to the generosity of Mr. John A. McDougald, who served as president in 1967. The coaching class is not only a spectacle of rare beauty but a test of driving skill as they are manoeuvred at a brisk trot through a tricky course of barrels.

When the new Horse Palace became available in 1931 everyone connected with the show was confident that it would accommodate all the horses that were likely to be shown in the foreseeable future. However as classes were added and the desire to show at the Royal increased, a stabling problem arose. To cope with it, and at the same time improve the show, eligibility requirements were imposed in the Hunter, Jumper and Junior divisions. Entries in these divisions were restricted to horses that had won prizes at recognized horse shows in the current year. Despite these restrictions, throughout the 60's there were invariably more entries than could be accommodated, and a shuttle service had to be adopted.

Stake prizes and trophies have always been important in stimulating the interest of exhibitors in the show. One thousand dollar stakes were first offered in 1927. The five to become available that year were: the Stillman Harness stake, donated by Mr. C. O. Stillman of Toronto; the McLaughlin Saddle stake, donated by Mr. R. S. McLaughlin of Oshawa; the Ellsworth Pony stake, donated by Mr. A. L. Ellsworth of Toronto; the Rogers stake, donated by Mr. Alfred Rogers of Toronto, and the Sir Clifford Sifton Jumping stake, donated by Sir Clifford Sifton of Toronto. The first time it was offered the Sir Clifford Sifton stake was won by Sir Clifford himself with a horse named Robin Hood.

In the years following, several stake classes were added. During his tenure of office as President, Col. Harry McGee created the President's Stake and established a precedent which subsequent Presidents have followed. (Since World War II, the price of immortality has increased 50 per cent, since the price of stakes rose in 1946 to $1,500.)

It may be difficult for those familiar with the present prize list to realize that there were only two trophies available at the first show. They were the King Edward Hotel trophy and the Governor-General's Cup. The King Edward Hotel trophy, donated by the hotel, was offered in a special class for high-steppers foaled in Canada. The trophy was to become the property of an exhibitor winning it three times, not necessarily in succession. It only lasted four years – Miss E. Viau of Montreal, with her horse, Lord Brilliant, won the class at the 1922, 1924 and 1925 shows.

When the trophy was replaced another outstanding horse was making his mark in the show ring. Temptation, owned by James Franceschini of Toronto, won the trophy in three straight years – in 1927, 1928 and 1929. Two horses, both owned by Mr. Franceschini were involved in the winning of the third trophy. Grand March won the class in 1930 and again in 1931, only to be placed second to his stablemate, Temptation, in 1932. Thus Mr. Franceschini won two of the three trophies donated by the King Edward Hotel.

The Governor-General's Cup has been offered at every Royal held to date. This coveted prize is awarded to the owner of the best three-year-old mare or gelding, bred in Canada, suitable for a military remount. The first winner of the trophy was Sir Adam Beck of London, the father of Hydro in Ontario, with a gelding name Denfield.

Several years later another award for hunters, the Lieutenant Governor's Cup became available. The conditions applicable to this class are similar to those in the Governor-General's Cup Class except that thoroughbreds are not eligible to compete.

In the late 20's and early 30's a number of other trophies were donated, some bore the names of living persons, but most were donated by relatives or friends in memory of people who had been actively associated with the Horse Show. Among these are the Sir Clifford Sifton Memorial trophy, the George W. Beardmore Memorial Challenge trophy, the James Widgery Memorial Challenge trophy, and the Captain Dick Paton Memorial Challenge trophy.

Some of the horses that established outstanding records were appropriately recognized at the end of their show careers. The first to be singularly honoured was Crystal Lady, a Hackney

Pony mare, owned by Mr. and Mrs. Elgin Armstrong of Brampton. On November 21, 1959, Crystal Lady, at the age of 15 years, standing 13 hands, was paraded into the ring with a large bouquet of roses over her back, while the band played "Auld Lang Syne," and received a final, formal farewell from the crowd in the arena. She had won 73 grand championships during her years in the show rings of North America. She was proclaimed World Harness Pony Champion in Chicago in 1948 and won the harness pony stake at the Royal for seven successive years, from 1947 to 1953.

Other famous horses to be recognized on their retirement were Patricia Valo, a Standard Bred mare that won a great many championships for her owner, Dr. E. E. Foster of Galt; King Clancy and Scarboro Princess, a pair of Hackneys that were the pride and joy of Lance Rumble of Toronto, and Blue Beau, a gelding which Mr. E. H. Coad of Aurora graciously loaned to the Canadian Equestrian team on several occasions, thereby enabling Canada to win many top awards in international competition.

Frequently attempts have been made to bolster attendance at the Horse Show by including special performances and non-competitive events.

At the first Royal, the star attraction was "California Frank's Mammoth Western Circus." California Frank was Frank Haffley and he was supported by a troupe that included his wife and daughter. Mrs. Haffley, known professionally as Maymie Francis, ran away from home at the age of 15 to join Buffalo Bill and was most famous for diving a horse from a 40-foot platform at Coney Island. Their daughter Reine boasted the titles of "World's champion horseback rifle shot" and "lady champion bronche-buster."

The most popular of all the Royal's special attractions undoubtedly has been the Musical Ride, performed in the early years by The Royal Canadian Dragoons under the direction of Major R. S. Timmis, and later by the Royal Canadian Mounted Police.

Among the novelty acts before the war were Christiansen's performing stallions and the Great Zacchini, who was shot from a cannon. Of a less spectacular nature were the sheep dog trials presented by Bill Martin of Maple Creek, Sask., the Halifax Children's Musical Ride, and demonstrations of dressage by Capt. Hiram E. Riley of Fort Riley, Kan.

In the post-war years some excellent attractions were presented. During the early 50's the famous Lipizzan stallions from the Spanish Riding School in Vienna were the feature. Meticulously trained, these stallions gave an exhibition of dressage as it is presented at the Olympic Competition Grand Prix. Other fine acts were presented by the Cadre Noir from the French Cavalry School at Saumur, France, and by Madame Hartel, an Olympic Medallist from Copenhagen. A polio victim in her youth, this courageous lady had to be lifted into the saddle for every performance.

In 1956, one of America's most popular radio and television artists, Mr. Arthur Godfrey, and his horse "Goldie" were the feature performers. To appear at the Royal and, at the same time maintain his busy broadcasting schedule, Mr. Godfrey had to fly back and forth between Toronto and New York. Since he wouldn't take any money for his appearances, the Royal presented him with a Hereford heifer to supplement the herd which he had established on his Virginia estate. Mr. Godfrey's act was so well received that he was invited back two years later, and again in 1962.

In 1964 and 1965, the spotlight was on Christilot Hanson, Canada's representative at the Olympic games in Tokyo. Riding her well-trained horse "Bonheur," she demonstrated the art of dressage in a manner that delighted her audiences.

Of all the special attractions that appeared during the post-war period none was more popular than the Musical Ride provided by the Royal Canadian Mounted Police. First presented in 1952 and back for repeat performances on many occasions thereafter, it became such a favourite with Toronto audiences that many patrons of the show wrote or telephoned to express their disappointment in the years that it was not scheduled to appear.

Tickets sales definitely increased in the years when big-name performers appeared at the Royal, but such talent was generally expensive and the greater revenue was seldom sufficient to offset the increased costs. In recent years, the Horse Show Committee has concentrated on improving the show, without special theatrical productions, and this policy has, in fact, produced higher net returns.

The Royal Agricultural Winter Fair has enjoyed royal patronage ever since it began and it has seemed appropriate at every fair to invite representatives of the reigning monarch – the Governor-General of Canada and the Lieutenant Governor of

Ontario – to pay an official visit to the Horse Show and tour the fair. These vice-regal visits are accompanied by all of the correct and colourful ceremonial, including the parading of honour guards with bands, royal salutes and formal inspections in the ring. These traditional manoeuvres never fail to be impressive, in spite of the fact that the footing in the tanbark ring is more reminiscent of the terrain of Flanders or North Africa than a neatly paved parade square. During the years most of the regiments, naval and air force contingents in the Toronto area, and the cadets of Royal Military College and Trinity College School, have had the opportunity of providing guards. From time to time, the Governor-General's Horse Guards have managed, by dint of raiding local riding stables, to turn out a mounted guard. On these special occasions, it has been customary for the occupants of box-seats and others to turn out in full evening dress – white tie, tails and top-hat, or hunting pinks, with their distinctive coloured collars marking the different hunts, and flashing military medals and orders. The ladies, of course, in their furs, jewels and couturier gowns are not to be outdone by masculine elegance. There is a great deal of animated visiting from box to box, tipping of top hats and saluting by officers of the guards and aides-de-camp. Even the chauffeurs, who traditionally gather at the southeast corner of the ring to smoke and exchange shop-talk while they wait to drive their employers to supper parties after the show, seem to enjoy the occasion.

In all, it is the most impressive congregation of Toronto society of the season and, in its glamour and opulence, is probably unique in North America, if not the world.

Since 1930, the social significance of the Royal Horse Show has been enhanced by the practice of inviting titled persons from Great Britain to participate in the judging of hunter classes. The first person to serve in this capacity was the Rt. Hon. Viscount Ebrington, M.C. of Gloucestershire, England. Since then a great many distinguished members of the peerage have graced the show. Throughout the years this has proven to be a providential arrangement. Not only have these gentlemen demonstrated their skill in judging horses but, in company with their charming wives, have contributed much to the social life of the Royal. One judge, His Grace, the Duke of Westminster, was so favourably impressed that he donated a beautiful trophy, made in the reign of King George III, for perpetual competition in the hunter division.

Private parties, some large and lavish, others small intimate dinners, are given by Toronto's leading hostesses in honour of Horse Show judges, exhibitors and out-of-town visitors, at which old friendships are renewed and new ones are made. It is also traditional for the Horse Show Committee to hold a large men's buffet luncheon. Undoubtedly these social activities have stimulated the demand for boxes which for many years has exceeded the number available.

Usually reports of these gatherings are published in the daily newspapers to the benefit of the Royal. Latterly sports editors and columnists have begun to display a keen interest in the Horse Show, and particularly the International Jumping events, with the result that competitive events are now receiving excellent coverage on the sports pages, a form of publicity which has helped to boost attendance.

A great deal of the credit for the success of the Horse Show should be given to the men who served on the Horse Show Administrative Committee, the senior governing body of the Horse Show. Although many of the details are delegated to the sub-committees of which there are five, namely, prize list, entry, international teams, ring and entertainment, the final decisions are made by the senior body.

Colonel H. C. Cox, who owned one of the finest show stables in the world, and whose horses performed brilliantly not only in Canada but in the United States and England as well, had the honour of being the first chairman of the Horse Show Administrative Committee. Others who served in that capacity during the pre-war period were: Mr. Alfred Rogers (1925-29); Major Clifford Sifton (1930-37), and Mr. John W. McKee (1938). When the fair was revived following the war, Mr. F. K. Morrow was appointed chairman; his successors were Major General C. C. Mann (1948-49); Lieutenant Colonel S. C. Bate (1950-54); Mr. J. H. Crang (1955-56); Mr. Trumbull Warren (1957-58); Brigadier F. C. Wallace (1959-60); Lieutenant Colonel Charles Baker (1961-63 and again in 1966); and Mr. W. A. Harris (1964-65).

These men were fortunate in having able men on their committees. Although there have been many changes in personnel, one man, Mr. John W. McKee, has served continuously on the Horse Show Administrative Committee since 1933. Two other men, Col. Clifford Sifton and Mr. Malcolm Richardson, who were members of the 1922 Committee are still actively associated with the Horse Show.

No record of the Royal Horse Show would be complete without specific reference to the late Major Widgery who, until his death in 1929, acted as Ringmaster. He was a man of great dignity, a charming personality and a strict disciplinarian. He was beloved by all exhibitors, many of whom he taught. In return he demanded the highest standard of deportment and dress in the ring. His memory is perpetuated by the James Widgery Challenge trophy competed for each year.

Another important personality was the late Captain Dick Paton who taught many young girls and boys the art of horsemanship and kept a fatherly eye on them both in the ring and out of it. Until his death in 1959, he was in charge of the assembly ring and contributed to the smooth running of the show. Many parents of today's exhibitors owe their love of horses and interest in riding to his influence and they in turn have passed on these characteristics to their children. He is remembered by the Captain Dick Paton Memorial Challenge trophy for Junior Conformation Hunters.

The Horse Show as we know it today is largely the result of innovations and policies introduced by the late Gordon Foxbar Perry who, as Vice-President and later as President, not only worked tirelessly but gave generously of his time and resources towards the improvement of the show.

Among the unsung heroes of horse shows held during the past 44 years are the men who directed activities in the ring. They learned from years of experience how to conduct the show with the utmost dispatch. As a result of the efficient way they carried out their duties the obstacles are set up for jumping classes and removed very expeditiously, thus avoiding any undue delay between classes.

On the basis of observations made during the past 45 years, it is quite apparent that the Horse Show and the Agricultural Show complement each other. Income from the sale of box and reserved seats at the Horse Show accounts for about one-third of the fair's income. There are substantial costs associated with the operation of the Horse Show but it shows a worth-while profit, which has been used to subsidize other phases of the show, suggesting that the founders of the Royal showed sound judgment in devising a complete and comprehensive show program.

According to the 1921 census, Canada's horse population totalled 3,624,300 head. At that time the steam engine was in its hey day. These wood or coal burning monsters provided the power to operate threshing machines, grain grinders and other belt-driven machines. Gasoline driven tractors were in the development stage. Horses, which had displaced oxen 50 years earlier, were the main source of power on farms, and most of the horses in Canada were of the heavy draught type.

Very few farmers, in fact few Canadians, owned motor cars in 1921, and good driving horses were a prized possession and essential for getting from one place to another. Every farmer owned one or more and it was not uncommon for city folk to own driving horses too. Standard Breds were the most popular breed for this purpose, although the more sophisticated preferred Hackneys. They couldn't move quite as fast but were a lot more graceful in their action.

Not all horses were used to take ladies to tea or for a turn around the park. Some of them brought the groceries to the back door and the barrels of beer to the bars. Department stores, bakeries and dairies were dependent on horses to deliver their products. These business people preferred horses weighing 1300-1400 pounds, with legs free of hair, to avoid picking up an extra burden of mud and snow. Farmers interested in catering to this market, practised cross-breeding, the most common crosses being Hackney or Thoroughbred stallions on Percheron mares. Occasionally Clydesdale mares were used as parent stock and usually the resultant progeny were satisfactory in body conformation, but frequently they were too hairy on the legs.

At that time heavy freight had to be moved from railway depots to its ultimate destination by horses-drawn drays. In every city there were one or more cartage firms, each of which used a great many heavy draught horses in its operations.

Ponies served a useful function too. Indulgent parents bought them to help their children develop a love for horses, and a knowledge of horsemanship – a socially desirable attitude and a practical skill. Shetlands were the "in" breed – in fact almost the only breed available in Canada, at that time.

Obviously horses were an important class of live stock in Canada in 1921. Not only did they supply power on farms, but because of their many other uses provided farmers with a cash income from the sale of surplus stock, particularly if that stock was of the type and quality in demand. There was good reason to emphasize breeding horse classes at the Royal. Naturally, priority was given to those breeds that were making the greatest contribution to the nation's economy.

In the heavy draught division there were classes for Clydesdales, Percherons, Belgians and Shires. From the standpoint of numbers, the Clydesdale was the most important breed. Many prominent horse breeders were importing stallions and mares, but particularly stallions, from Scotland, the country where the Clydesdale originated. Competition at the first few Royals was such that two classifications were provided – one for Canadian breds, the other an open class. As expected, most of the entries in the open class were imported.

Percherons and Belgians, breeds that originated in France and Belgium respectively, were just beginning to become popular in 1921. Since most of the original settlers in Canada came from the British Isles, they and their descendants were inclined to favour a breed that originated in their homeland. This personal preference gave Clydesdales a distinct advantage over the other two breeds. Their enthusiastic supporters claimed that Clydesdales had more quality of legs and feet than other breeds and tried to clinch their argument by coining the phrase "no feet and legs, no horse," meaning that unless a horse has good legs and feet it isn't of much value. At it turned out this catch-phrase was practised too assiduously. Twenty-five years later a great many Clydesdales excelled in feet and legs but were sadly lacking in substance and muscling. In the interval Percheron and Belgian breeders had concentrated on improving the underpinning of their horses and at the same time retaining their massive body conformation.

Although the Shire was developed in England it was never popular in Canada, even among people who had migrated from that country. Shires were draughty in conformation, but this was offset by the extreme hairiness on their legs, a characteristic which proved to be a disadvantage in mud or snow. Classes were provided for this breed at the first Royal, but there were very few exhibitors. In the years following interest gradually declined, so the classification for Shires was withdrawn in 1930.

After World War I a few Canadians began to import and raise Suffolk horses, an English breed that resembles the Belgian in many respects. At the request of the breeders a classification was established in 1928. However the competition was so disappointing that classes were discontinued after a one-year trial.

The French Canadian has the distinction of being the only breed of horses developed in Canada. Mature horses usually weigh 1,000-1,100 pounds. They are sturdily built, hence capable of doing light farm work, particularly on the small family farms of Quebec. In addition they can be used as road horses. However the breed never became popular outside its native province. Despite this fact classes for French Canadian horses were provided at the first Royal and repeated until 1960, by which time competition ceased to exist.

During the late 1920's Boys' Colt Clubs were organized throughout the province under the auspices of the Ontario Department of Agriculture. They were so popular that a provincial competition was established at the Royal in 1932. Competition was limited to the top prize winners at local clubs' Achievement Days. Even so, it was not uncommon for 50-60 colts to be shown at the Royal. These competitions were continued until 1938, but were not revived after the war.

During the 1920's great advances were made in the production of farm tractors. The two cylinder iron-horses of an earlier period were replaced by more refined models, designed to suit conditions in Eastern Canada. As the country became more prosperous, tractors began to displace horses on many farms. However, this trend was halted in 1930, with the beginning of the Depression. Farmers did not have money to buy tractors, in fact many did not have the means to buy gasoline for the tractors they owned. Consequently the mechanical threat to the horse came to a sudden, if temporary, end.

By 1939, however, Canada was at war. Men were leaving the farms to join the armed forces, or to work in war industries. The government pledged the country to supply vast quantities of foodstuffs to Great Britain and the allied armies. To meet these requirements farmers were obliged to mechanize. Tractors and other machines were rationed but steps were taken to put available equipment in the hands of farmers who were best able to use it.

The real trend toward mechanization began after the war. With machinery companies reverting to peace-time production, tractors were being produced in record quantities. With the lifting of controls, prices of farm products increased and farmers could afford to buy more tractors and machinery. As the number of tractors increased the horse population declined, finally reaching a record low of about 400,000 in 1966. By that year, draught horses had practically disappeared from the farm scene. Nevertheless the Royal continued to provide classes for the three draught breeds. A great many people are speculating on how long this practice can continue in an age when so much emphasis is being placed on utility.

In the hey-day of draught horses, a few outstanding stallions helped to make heavy horse history. Prominent among the Clydesdale champions were Arnprior Emigrant, owned by the Reston Syndicate of Manitoba, Lochinvar, a winner of many championships for Jock Falconer of Saskatchewan, and Brunstane Zenith, a stallion that attained his greatest prominence while owned by Ben Rothwell of Ottawa. The very first award presented at the Royal was to Bolle Ile Sensation, a Clydesdale stallion shown by the Manitoba Department of Agriculture.

Among the noted Percheron stallions were Monarch, owned by Carl Roberts of Manitoba, Fairview King, owned by Archie Haas of Paris, and Captivator, owned by National Breweries of Montreal. At one time this company owned over 20 stallions, which were shown at most exhibitions in Canada. (By a happy coincidence all of these horses were black, providing their sponsor with one of Canada's first "live" commercials.)

The most prominent Belgian exhibitors for many years were Gilbert Arnold of Quebec and Archie Haas of Paris. Their most famous stallions were Dock, Carman Dale and West Pine Supreme, the latter two being owned by Haas.

Although the heavy horse population has experienced a very sharp decline in the past 45 years, interest in light horses moved in the other direction, a trend which has been reflected in the breeding horse classification at the Royal. In reviewing developments it is quite apparent that the changes made were based on economic considerations. In 1922 the three principal light horse breeds at the show were Standard Breds, Thoroughbreds and Hackneys – the most popular motive power with the "carriage trade." At that time horse racing was not the popular sport it is today. Trotting races were restricted to country fairs, while flat racing was considered a rich man's hobby. Type, conformation and soundness were the primary factors in selecting breeding stock. Speed was seldom considered.

In the post-war years, however, racing became a popular

"spectator sport" (even though most of the "spectators" never got very far past the pari-mutual wicket). Ability to move at great speed became a prime requisite. In fact, type and conformation were often subordinated to speed in the selection of breeding stock. As this tendency developed the standard of the horses entered in the Standard Bred and Thoroughbred classes declined, presumably because many of the good horses were in training or racing at the time shows were held.

During the 1920's a great many people became interested in hunting, creating a demand for horses that combined the attributes of being comfortable to ride and capable of jumping. The demand reached significant proportions about the time farmers began replacing draught horses with tractors. Those inclined to breed a few mares each year were encouraged to mate their heavy draught females to Thoroughbred stallions with a view to selling the progeny as hunters. While many of the first generation offspring were unsuitable for this purpose, excellent results were obtained when the cross-breds were mated back to Thoroughbreds.

Much of the credit for this development should be given to the Canadian Hunter and Light Horse Improvement Association, an organization formed in the early 30's, and, in the early stages, to Departments of Agriculture. The Royal played an important role too by adding a Light Horse Improvement Division, thereby providing an opportunity for breeders to display and compare their stock. Following the addition of this division, several classes for Hunters were added to the Horse Show.

No further expansion in the classification took place until after the war. In 1946, classes for Saddle Horses and Palominos were added and in the years following, the Breeding Horse Division was augmented by classes for Arabians, Welsh Ponies, and Quarter Horses. Interest in Quarter Horses increased very rapidly and there were more of them than of any other breed at the 1966 Royal.

Changes in production practices have been reflected not only in the types of horses shown but also in the personnel of the Breeding Horse Committees of 1922 and 1966. In 1922 most of the members represented the heavy draught breeds. Among them were William Smith and E. H. C. Tisdale, two charter members of the Royal, and Walter Scott, who served on the Executive Committee in the 1920's. As new breeds were added representation was granted to the breed associations concerned.

As a result the most members are now representatives of the light horse breeds. Despite the changes in personnel, there has been no change in the primary objective of the committee: to encourage and promote the production of good horses.

LIVESTOCK

Cattle exhibitors in 1960 found this "five-minute cow wash" a convenient addition to the show

Two boys make friends with a new calf

Class for aged Jerseys
at the first
Royal, 1922

Shampooing an
Ayrshire

"Montvic Rag Apple
Marksman," one of
Canada's most famous
Holstein bulls

Grand Champion Short-
horn bull, shown by
H.R.H. Prince of Wales
Ranch in 1925, had
the unlikely name
"King of the Fairies"

First cattle arrive
from the West

"Black Billy," Grand
Champion Steer, 1923,
shown with
Raymond Clarkson

This Holstein cow sold
at auction for $16,500

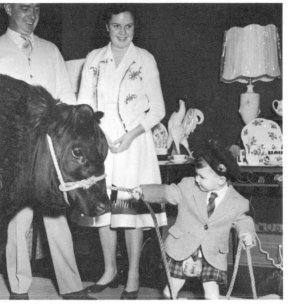

LEFT: Champion steers, carcass class

RIGHT: The proverbial bull in a china shop

Auction sale of steers

J. D. Brien, General
Superintendent, 1922-46

LEFT: John McKee, first
Chairman of the
Cattle Committee

CENTRE: J. M. Gardhouse,
Shorthorn breeder and
one of the founders

RIGHT: L. O. Clifford,
Hereford breeder,
Charter Member and
first Chairman of
the Beef Committee

Judge Charlie Yule of
Calgary and herdsman
Fred Major of Uni-
versity of Alberta
choosing the Grand
Champion Steer

The Dairy Cattle
Committee, 1947

Old-timer Pete McEwen
presents the Empire
Challenge cup

The sheep-shearing
contest

Grand Champion
wether, 1926

A quick snack shared
in the sleeping
quarters

Herdsman caught
napping

CHAPTER 3 Livestock

MA N Y of the beef cattle exhibitors at the first Royal were members of the second generation in the business. As the result of paternal training they were able to exert a profound influence on the development of their respective breeds in the early part of the century. The names of Will Dryden of Brooklin, John Miller, Jr. of Ashburn, James Watt of Elora, James Douglas of Caledonia, John Gardhouse of Weston, T. A. Russell of Downsview, Duncan Campbell of Moffat, Thomas Amos of Moffat and Harry McGee of Islington, all Shorthorn breeders, will long be remembered.

Among the noted Hereford breeders were L. O. Clifford of Oshawa, McNeil and McNeil of Dutton, A. A. MacDonald of Kirkfield, and Frank Collacutt of Crossfield, Alberta. The principal Aberdeen Angus exhibitors in those early days were James Bowman of Guelph, J. D. Larkin of Queenston, S. C. Channon of Oakwood, John Lowe of Elora, George McAllister of Guelph, and J. D. McGregor of Brandon, Manitoba.

All of these outstanding breeders are now dead, and it seems a tragedy that few of their descendants are carrying on in the family tradition. Actually only one direct descendant of the beef cattle exhibitors at the first show participated in the centennial year Royal, namely Reford Gardhouse, a grandson of the founder of the herd of John Gardhouse and Sons of Weston.

At the first show two rank amateurs had the audacity to challenge the old line professionals. They were Russell Parker and his cousin Alex Edwards, both of Watford, who showed steers under the name Parker and Edwards. Although they didn't win many prizes the experience proved to be invaluable. In the years following both developed outstanding herds – Parker with Shorthorns and Edwards with Aberdeen Angus. Furthermore both have exhibited at every Royal held to date.

Aside from the fact that very few members of the present generation have followed in the footsteps of their ancestors, there have been many other changes in the beef cattle industry and in this particular division of the show during the past 45 years. In 1922, the Shorthorn was the most prominent breed of beef cattle in Canada. Two decades later Shorthorns were outnumbered by Herefords and were being rapidly overtaken by Aberdeen Angus. By 1967, Hereford registrations were almost double the combined total of the other two breeds and Angus registrations were significantly above those of Shorthorns.

At the first Royal, and for a number of years thereafter, the prize money for Shorthorns was well above that of the other two breeds, largely because of the generous grant made by the Dominion Shorthorn Association. Shorthorn breeders competed for prizes totalling $3,612, while Hereford and Angus breeders were offered $1,637 and $1,310 respectively.

This wide disparity in prize money was narrowed as the grants from the Hereford and Angus Associations were increased. Despite the growth and development of these two breeds, Shorthorns continued to receive the largest share of the prize money. In 1958, however, a committee was appointed under the chairmanship of the author of this history, who at the time was Live Stock Commissioner of Ontario, to review the situation. After considering all the facts, the committee recommended that the Royal establish a basic prize offering for each breed and that it offer to match the grant made by each breed association.

The Executive Committee of the Royal endorsed these recommendations, and the basic offering for each breed was established at $1,800. Since each breed association agreed to make a grant of $1,400, the total offering per breed amounted to $4,600. From 1960 to 1963, the Royal had higher-than-average operating profits, and was able to authorize a general increase in the prize money. In the allocation which followed, the basic offering for each beef breed was increased by $300.

Throughout the years, beef breed associations have subscribed to the principle of a uniform classification. Undoubtedly agreement on this point has been achieved by delegating responsibility for drafting the classification to the Joint Beef Breeds

Association, an organization comprised of representatives of the three beef breed associations.

Although uniform classifications were adopted each year, they have been subject to change from time to time. It is interesting to note that classes were provided for aged bulls and aged cows at the first Royal, despite the fact that many breeders argued against staging these classes on the grounds that mature animals should be maintained in good breeding condition in their respective herds instead of being fitted and in some cases over-fitted for shows. These classes were continued until 1946.

Other changes in the classification, before 1965, were minor. The most significant involved splitting the yearlings into three divisions – senior, summer and junior. Invariably the changes resulted in an increase in the number of classes per breed. In fact, by 1964 there were 14 classes for single animals, and 4 group classes.

In that year the Hon. Harry Hays, Minister of Agriculture for Canada, announced a new policy of federal assistance to fairs. When making the announcement he expressed the opinion that both exhibitors and spectators were losing interest in agricultural fairs. He attributed the decline in exhibitor interest to the fact that prize offerings had not kept pace with the increase in the cost of exhibiting. Lack of interest, which in some cases bordered on indifference, on the part of spectators, was ascribed to the classifications which in his opinion were too complex and tended to emphasize frills rather than utility.

The new policy was designed to correct these weaknesses. In order to bolster prizes, the Minister offered to duplicate the offering at shows that adopted the classification proposed by his Department. In the hope of enticing more breeders to exhibit, fairs were required to impose a limit on the number of animals that any one person could show. To stimulate interest among spectators, the number of classes per breed was reduced to seven – three for bulls, three for females and one for a group comprised of four animals, bred and owned by the exhibitor.

These proposals were carefully considered at the 1964 meeting of the Royal's Beef Cattle Committee and were rejected on the grounds that they were much too radical. However, the prospect of additional prize money proved to be very alluring to the management of a number of other shows in Canada. As a result, the program was accepted as a pilot project at those shows. As might be expected, the reactions of exhibitors were mixed. Most of them were not enthusiastic about the reduction in classes and the limitation on entries, but they did appreciate the experience of winning more prize money with fewer cattle.

When the subject came up for discussion the next year, the committee agreed to accept the policy. From the standpoint of the Royal, the results were disappointing. For the first time in years there were empty stalls in the cattle barn. On the other hand, there was an increase in the number of exhibitors and competition in all classes was very keen.

The Royal has played an important role in the field of animal health. In 1922 there were relatively few tuberculosis-free herds in Canada. Owners of such herds were reluctant to exhibit, unless they were protected against the possibility of infection. At the first show, the TB-free herds were segregated from the others, a feat which was accomplished by stabling each class of cattle in separate barns.

By 1927, when the new cattle barn was ready for occupancy, segregation by this method was no longer possible and all cattle except those originating in TB-free herds, were required to be negative to a TB test conducted within 30 days of the commencement of the show. The Health of Animals Branch of the Federal Department of Agriculture agreed to conduct the necessary tests at no cost to the exhibitors. Undoubtedly this requirement stimulated interest in the TB eradication program. During the next few years, there was a sharp increase in the number of herds enrolled under the accredited herd policy. The program was expanded to include the testing of all cattle in prescribed areas. By the late 1930's, Canada became, for all practical purposes, a TB free country. Although the rule respecting TB tests is still in effect, it has lost much of its meaning, because of the progress that has been made in stamping out the disease.

In 1937 another disease, Brucellosis, or Bang's disease, was causing cattlemen a great deal of concern and, it became mandatory in that year for all cattle at the Royal to be negative to a Bang's disease test conducted within 30 days of the fair. Breeders began to establish tested herds, that is, herds certified free of the disease. This was followed by an area eradication program. Progress in eliminating this disease has been very rapid by comparison with the time required to eradicate Tuberculosis.

Those associated with the Royal can derive a great deal of satisfaction from the fact that this show rendered a valuable service to the live stock industry by stimulating the expansion of disease eradication programs. Equally important, however, the Royal is indebted to officials of the Health of Animals Branch of the Canada Department of Agriculture for their services in conducting tests in cases where tests were required and in supervising the health of animals during the time they were at the show.

When the first show was held and for years thereafter it was common practice for an exhibitor to bring along three or four cows, usually of dairy breeding, to act as nursemaids to his junior and, in some cases, senior calves. Although these "nurse cows" were not eligible to compete, the owner was charged a fee of $2.50 per cow. Because of their unsightly appearance, it was considered advisable to stable them in an area screened from the general public.

As entries in the beef cattle division increased, the number of nurse cows brought to the show increased as well. The problem of finding suitable accommodation for them became greater. In an effort to discourage breeders from bringing nurse cows to the fair, the fee was increased to $3.00 in 1949, $5.00 in 1950, $7.00 in 1953, and finally to $12.00 in 1956.

By the time the final increase was imposed most breeders had reached the conclusion that it was uneconomical to use two cows, the mother and a foster mother, to raise one calf. Consequently, by mutual agreement among the exhibitors, and much to the relief of management, the use of nurse cows at the Royal was prohibited in 1960.

During the early years of the Royal some unsavory rumours about unethical fitting were circulated in the cattle barns. The perpetrators of these rumours were no respecters of persons, with the result that a cloud of suspicion was cast over all exhibitors.

Among the practices considered to be unethical, the most common were the cutting of ties on the backs of cattle, particularly in Herefords, a breed which at that time was addicted to this condition, and the injection of liquid wax or other foreign substance into depressed areas thereby creating a smooth, well fleshed appearance on animals which in their natural state lacked filling in certain areas of their bodies.

In 1926 the directors adopted a rule prohibiting these unethical practices and imposed severe penalties. Arrangements were made for officers of the Health of Animals Branch, Canada Department of Agriculture, to enforce the rule. In order to carry out this assignment, all cattle, both beef and dairy, are inspected prior to entering the judging ring. To the credit of the exhibitors it must be said that very few cases of unethical fitting have been uncovered since 1926.

No history of the beef cattle division would be complete without some reference to the trends in type and conformation that have taken place in the past 44 years. In 1922, a typical Shorthorn was large, fairly thick, with the older animals inclined to be patchy around the tail head. Herefords possessed similar characters. Generally speaking, however, they had heavy front quarters and lacked thickness in the hind quarters. Animals of both breeds had good inherent ability to convert roughage into beef.

On the other hand, a typical Angus was smaller, more blocky, lower set, and decidedly smoother in its fleshing. Because of its superiority in these respects, the Angus were fairly consistent winners in the steer classes. Being conscious and perhaps envious of this, Shorthorn breeders, and to a lesser extent Hereford breeders, began striving to produce animals that resembled the Angus in type and conformation. They were aided and abetted in their efforts by the Depression, when people had little money to spend and were looking for small cuts of beef. The net result was that, within a few years, Shorthorn cattle became considerably smaller and in the process lost some of their ability to convert feed into beef efficiently. While the same practices were followed by Hereford breeders, the trend towards smaller cattle was arrested sooner. In any event compact cattle were winning top honours in all beef breeds during the pre-war years.

In the post-war years, characterized by an affluent society, small cuts lost their appeal. Scientists had discovered that rate of gain is a hereditary characteristic and that animals which make the fastest gain usually make the most economical gain. Consequently, today the trend is towards larger, growthier animals and, fortunately, breeders are achieving their objective in this regard without sacrificing quality.

Dual Purpose Shorthorns

In 1922 Dual Purpose Shorthorns were fairly popular in Canada, but particularly in Eastern Canada. The breed was considered well suited for mixed farm operations. The cows were capable of producing a considerable quantity of milk and of raising calves which, while not as blocky and low-set as the progeny of beef cows, were capable of developing into acceptable beef animals. Therefore the breed found a great deal of favour among farmers

84

whose main sources of income were derived from the sale of beef, cream, hogs and poultry.

Under the circumstances it was only natural that a classification should be provided for this breed. At the outset, it was classified as a beef breed, but it was never accepted as an equal partner with the other beef breeds. The classification did not include as many sections nor was the prize offering as attractive.

Ever zealous of the milk-producing capabilities of the breed and anxious to preserve them, the breeders insisted on restricting the showing of males to bulls out of dams with R.O.P. records of sired by bulls out of dams with R.O.P. records. For a number of years similar requirements applied to the showing of heifers under three years of age.

After the war, farmers became more specialized. Those engaged in milk production, regardless of the form in which the product was sold, became partial to the breeds with the greatest production potential. Farmers intent on beef production were inclined to favour the most efficient beef breeds. Thus Dual Purpose numbers began to decline, and exhibits at the Royal followed a similar trend.

Under the classifications adopted in 1965, Dual Purpose Shorthorns were classed as dairy cattle and were subjected to the production requirements that applied to the other dairy breeds. Since many potential show animals could not meet these requirements, the number of animals shown in 1965 registered a sharp decline from previous years.

Red Polls
The Red Poll breed showed signs of achieving a fair degree of popularity in the late 1940's. While membership in the Red Poll Association was not large, the breed was national in scope, by virtue of the fact that there were breeders in all of the principal cattle-producing provinces. Under the circumstances the Royal agreed to provide classes in 1951.

When farmers started to specialize, this breed also became a victim of the trend. Latterly exhibits have declined, both in numbers and in quality, many of the animals being of mediocre type or carrying a great deal less fit than that expected of show cattle. Hence the classification for this breed was dropped in 1966.

French Canadians
The French Canadian is the only breed of cattle of Canadian

origin. It was developed to meet conditions prevailing in parts of Quebec. Being comparatively small in size it was acclaimed as being capable of converting feed into milk quite economically.

Classes for this breed were provided at the first show and for years thereafter. However the numbers on exhibit and the number of breeders participating declined with each passing year. In 1959, by which time entries had dwindled to token numbers, the classification for this breed was also discontinued.

The Beef Cattle Committee

Throughout the years the Royal has been fortunate in having men who were outstanding in their respective fields serve on the various committees. In this connection, some of the most progressive thinking originated with the Beef Cattle Committee. The first chairman was L. O. Clifford of Oshawa, a Hereford breeder, who represented Ontario County in the House of Commons for several years. He was succeeded in 1927 by J. M. Gardhouse of Weston, a Shorthorn breeder and an outstanding judge of beef cattle, draught horses and sheep. F. C. Fletcher, Manager of the Union Stock Yards, and one of the founders of the Royal, became chairman in 1933. He was followed in 1938 by Howard Fraleigh of Forest, Ont., a prominent producer and exhibitor of market cattle.

When the Royal resumed after the war, W. J. Russell of Unionville, a Shorthorn breeder, was appointed chairman and continued to serve in that capacity for several years. When he retired, it became an unwritten law that no chairman should serve for more than three years and that the chairmanship should be alternated between representatives of the three beef breeds. During the next nine years, J. R. Kohler, George Rodanz, and Reford Gardhouse, Aberdeen Angus, Hereford and Shorthorn breeders respectively, served as chairmen, each for a three-year term.

Since then the term of office has been reduced to two years. The latest chairmen were Tom Jackson, Glen Reicheld and Norman Hogg.

MARKET CATTLE

At the time of the first Royal and for several years thereafter, well-finished steers weighing 1,300 - 1,400 pounds commanded top prices on Canadian markets. Invariably these steers were bought for export to the United States or Great Britain where the demand for steers in this weight range was greater than in Canada. Because of this situation, it was common practice for beef cattle producers and feeders to market their cattle at three years of age.

In the late 1920's, the U.S. government imposed a restrictive tariff on Canadian cattle and cattle shipments to the U.S. declined to a mere trickle. This action sent prices down, but the real slump didn't come until Canada was plunged into a depression in late 1929. During the next seven years the cattle industry was in the doldrums. With export markets practically non-existent, cattle had to be sold at sacrifice prices. Cattlemen were encouraged to market their cattle at younger ages and lighter weights. Three-year-old cattle became a relic of the past. Instead farmers started marketing their cattle as two-year-olds and in some cases as baby beeves.

By 1937 economic conditions had begun to improve. The U.S. tariff was lowered, and Canadian cattle were permitted to enter on more favourable terms. Although price ceilings were imposed during the war years, there was a ready market for all the beef that could be produced. Since then, except for 1952-53 when cattle and beef were shut off from all outside markets because of an outbreak of Foot-and-Mouth disease, Canadian cattlemen have shaped their production programs to meet U.S. market demands.

These trends in market conditions have had a distinct bearing on the classification for market cattle at the Royal. In the earlier years classes were provided for steers in the heavier weight ranges, but as the demand for younger and lighter cattle increased the classification was revised accordingly. At one time heifers were eligible to show in classes for market cattle under 900 pounds, but very few were shown. Consequently, in 1955, the privilege of showing heifers was withdrawn.

From the outset separate classes were established for Aberdeen Angus, Herefords, Shorthorns and grades or cross-breds. Originally all steers or heifers were classified according to age. However, in 1930 and for a number of years thereafter, grades or cross-breds were classified on the basis of weight. Later, with weight-for-age becoming recognized as an important economic consideration, the original basis was re-instated.

Grand Champion Steer
Ever since the Royal began, the winning of the Grand Champion

Steer award has been one of the most coveted prizes at the show. (The names of the successful exhibitors and the breeders of the steers shown by them are listed in the Appendix.) Of the 25 exhibitors who have won this award, the most frequent, with nine championships, was the University of Alberta. Most of their champions were fitted by Fred Major, who was the university herdsman for many years and twice judged steers at the Royal. Five breeders have two championships to their credit: J. M. Gardhouse, Lloyd Mack, Leo Halstead, Carr Hatch and Ed Noad.

Undoubtedly interest in the steer classes has been stimulated by the prices paid for the champions. Actually no sensational prices were received before the war, champions seldom selling for more than $1.50 per pound. In 1946, however, the Grand Champion Steer was auctioned in the main arena during the Horse Show. This proved to be an entertaining feature for the spectators, but a nightmare for the auctioneers and buyers. At that sale, the champion, a Hereford steer from the herd of Fred Reicheld & Son of Jarvis, brought the fantastic price of $13.00 per pound from the T. Eaton Company of Toronto. This record stood until 1965 when the champion, an Aberdeen Angus, was knocked down to Dominion Stores Limited at the same figure. In 1966 the record was broken when the Grand Champion Steer, shown by DeSoudry Construction Ltd. of West Shefford, Que., an Angus, was bought by Dominion Stores for $13.25 a pound.

In 1947 the sale was again held during the Horse Show. However the bidding got completely out of hand. Potential buyers, sensing that they were bidding against people who had no interest in obtaining the steer and who in many cases did not realize what they were doing, registered their disapproval. Since then the Grand Champion Steer has been the headliner at the regular sale of market cattle.

Prices tapered off during the next few years but took an upward turn in the 1960's. In 1962, Marion and Don Johnson, a young couple from Burrows, Sask., received $12.50 per pound for their champion and used the money received for this steer to pay off the mortgage on the farm they had recently acquired. Other recipients of high prices were Leo Halstead who received $10.00 and $11.00 per pound respectively for his champions in 1960 and 1961. The 1963 champion, owned jointly by Angus Glen Farms of Unionville, Ont., and Marvin Hinton of Mount Stirling, Ohio, brought $11.75 per pound, while Meadow Lane

Farm's champion of 1964 sold for $11.00 per pound. Although bidding for all of these champions was quite keen, the purchaser, in each case, was Dominion Stores Limited of Toronto. To the disappointment of many, but particularly to those directly involved, the prices received for the Reserve Champions were very modest by comparison.

Because of the financial reward accruing to the exhibitor of the champion, the man chosen to make the awards has been placed in a position of grave responsibility. From a monetary standpoint the difference between winning a championship and a reserve championship has amounted to several thousand dollars. The Royal has been fortunate in its selection of judges and has spared no effort to obtain the services of the best men available.

Before the war it was common practice to have the Aberdeen Angus, Hereford and Shorthorn steers, judged by the same men who judged the breeding classes. The grades or cross-breds were judged by men associated with the packing house industry. At the first Royal, the judges for Angus, Hereford and Shorthorn steers were Stanley Pierce of Creston, Ill., John Van Natta of Lafayette, Ind., and Dean C. F. Curtis of Ames, Ia., respectively. The grades or cross-breds were judged by T. A. Inguerson of Swift & Company, Chicago. In the years following many prominent U.S. cattle breeders served as judges. On two occasions, however, the classes were judged by well-known British breeders, namely R. F. P. Duncan and Walter Biggar. Mr. Biggar had the distinction of judging steers at the Chicago International for several consecutive years during the 1930's.

Since the war, men other than breed judges have been selected to place the steer classes. In 1946, Mr. Charles Yule, Manager of the Calgary Stampede for many years, was chosen for this assignment. He was invited back in 1948, in 1950, and for the next seven years.

Among others to officiate in the post-war period were: Dr. Grant McEwan, later Lieutenant Governor of Alberta; Fred Major of London, Ont.; Tom Scott of Ninga, Man.; John Hay of Nanton, Alta.; Dick Sour of Urbana, Ohio; and Bill Cameron of Midnapore, Alta.

Although most of the attention has been focussed on the classes for individual steers, group classes have formed an important part of the program. Originally the classes called for groups of three steers, with weight being the deciding factor in determining the class in which the animals were shown. In 1926 a class for six steers or heifers was added. One of the conditions of entry required that all animals be polled (dehorned). This sparked a great deal of controversy. However the advocates of this policy succeeded in having the rule applied to all group classes thereafter. Despite their claims that this rule should apply to all steers, it did not become mandatory for steers entered in single classes to be hornless until 1951, and then only after one year's notice had been given.

A carlot competition was introduced in 1929, with the exhibit to be comprised of 15 steers of a weight not exceeding 1,200 pounds. In 1947, the class was split into two divisions: one for steers weighing under 1,100 pounds, the other for steers 1,101-1,300 pounds. A year later the maximum weight was reduced to 1,250 pounds and the number of steers to be included in a group was reduced from 15 to 12. McIntyre Ranching Company of Lethbridge, Alta., has been a consistent winner in the carlot classes.

Carcass Classes
The look of a beef animal in the ring can be deceptive. You can't really be sure of its quality until it has been butchered. These facts were recognized by members of the Market Cattle Committee during the early years of the Royal. However, it was not until 1935 that classes for beef carcasses were provided.

Originally steers shown on the hoof were eligible for the carcass classes. Following the live judging, the steers were removed to a packing plant for slaughter. After being properly chilled the carcasses were judged and the champion carcass was brought back and displayed at the fair in a portable cooler.

In 1947 permanent refrigerators were installed in the area now known as the Meat Arcade. More carcass classes were added, and the privilege of showing in both live and carcass classes was withdrawn. Steers entered in the carcass classes are now delivered two days before the opening of the fair, and it is possible to have them slaughtered before the show opens and the carcasses displayed throughout the fair.

The beef cattle classification proposed by the Hon. Harry Hays contains an Interbreed Steer Class under which the awards are based on a combination of live appraisal, carcass appraisal and weight-per-day-of-age. This class, introduced at the 1965

Royal, was first won by Alex Orde of Guelph with a steer that ranked first in both live and carcass appraisal, a tribute to the skill of experienced judges in picking good beef while it is still on the hoof.

Committee Chairmen

Frank C. Fletcher was keenly interested in the marketing of live stock, and at the same time as he was organizing the Royal, he took an active part in setting up this division. Furthermore he committed his company to make generous grants to the Royal for a period of 10 years. Under the circumstances he was the natural choice for chairman of the first Market Live Stock Committee.

In 1929 S. E. Todd, Managing Director of the Industrial and Development Council of Canadian Meat Packers, later renamed the Meat Packers Council, was appointed Chairman and continued to serve in that capacity until 1946. In the following year he retired from active service on the Council and severed his connection with the committee. Mr. Fletcher was re-appointed Chairman and continued to serve faithfully for the next five years.

Since then men who have occupied the chairmanship of this committee with distinction include: Earl S. Manning, Mr. Todd's successor as Managing Director of the Meat Packers Council; Fred M. Campbell, Mr. Fletcher's successor as Manager of the Stock Yards; Frank E. Wolff, of the Agricultural Department, Canadian Pacific Railway; R. H. Graham, former Live Stock Commissioner for Ontario; H. K. Leckie, the present Managing Director of the Meat Packers Council; and H. E. McGill, Live Stock Commissioner for Ontario.

The Market Live Stock Committee has had fewer chairmen than most other committees. Furthermore, none of the men who served in that capacity was a producer of market cattle — for good and proper reasons. The chairman of the Market Cattle Committee must perform such regular duties as are expected of the chairman of any other committee. In addition, however, he must arrange for decisions of the committee to be carried out. To do this effectively he should be familiar with the operation of stock yards and packing plants and be personally acquainted with the men in charge of operations at these establishments.

Despite the fact that producers have been denied the honour of serving as chairman, they have been ably represented on the committee. As a general rule, half the members have been prominent exhibitors, while the rest were representatives of allied industries and departments of agriculture. By pooling their talents they have developed programs which have proven extremely beneficial to beef producers.

DAIRY CATTLE

No man occupied the position of chairman of a committee at the Royal for a longer time than John McKee of Norwich. One of the founders of the fair and a prominent Ayrshire breeder, Mr. McKee was appointed chairman of the Dairy Cattle Committee in 1922 and continued to serve in that capacity throughout the entire pre-war period, guiding the affairs of the committee during the most critical period of its existence.

When the fair was resumed following the war, it was agreed that the chairman's term of office should not exceed three years and that the position should alternate between representatives of the four leading dairy breeds. Since that decision was made, the committee has been headed by P. L. Whytock (1946-48); Hugh Hill (1949-51); George W. Henry (1952-54); J. D. Lanthier (1955-57); W. D. Thompson (1958-60); W. S. Brooks (1961-63); D. S. Dunton, 1964; R. O. Biggs, 1965 and Francis Redelmeier, 1966-67.

Classes were provided at the first show for six breeds: Ayrshires, Brown Swiss, French Canadians, Guernseys, Holsteins and Jerseys. Apparently there were very few entries in the Brown Swiss classes and only a slight prospect of any increase in competition. In any event, the classes for this breed were discontinued after being offered for one year. The French Canadian breed suffered a similar fate, but the end did not come as suddenly. Although there were only two exhibitors of French Canadian cattle at the first show, the classification for this breed was continued until 1959. In the interval there was an appreciable increase in entries, followed by a sharp decline. By the time the classification was dropped, competition, for all practical purposes, ceased to exist.

Since 1922 the classification for the four major breeds has been fairly uniform, with a few minor variations. At first there were 15 classes for single animals and five for groups, but in the years following there was a tendency for breed associations to recommend additional classes.

The first significant increase materialized in 1923 when

production classes were added. To be eligible to show in these classes, bulls, had to be out of dams with R.O.P. records, and cows four years of age and over had to have official records in their own right. However, animals shown in the regular classes were eligible to compete, provided they could comply with the production qualifications. In determining the standing of the animals a maximum of 70 points were allotted for type and 30 points for production. The judges placed the animals in each class in descending order of merit and allotted a score to each individual, while a clerk determined their production rating. The final placings were made on the basis of the total scores for the two factors.

Production classes as such were discontinued in 1928. Coincidentally, however, production records became a condition of entry in the two youngest bull classes. In 1933, Hon. Robert Weir, Minister of Agriculture for Canada, announced a policy of assistance to fairs, to focus more attention on production. Although production records were not a condition of entry at the Royal, animals without records or out of non-record dams, in the the case of bulls and young females, were penalized, their owners being eligible for only 80 per cent of the prize money offered. In 1946, the Holstein-Friesian Association of Canada opposed the policy and succeeded in having the production requirements withdrawn from the rules respecting that breed. The other dairy breed associations took a similar stand the following year.

Between 1947 and 1965 production records were not a condition of entry in the dairy cattle classes at the Royal. Undoubtedly this situation gave critics an opportunity to proclaim that fairs were more interested in frills than in utility. Spurred on by these remarks the Dairy Cattle Committee, somewhat reluctantly, recommended the adoption of the classification proposed by the Hon. Harry Hayes in 1965. This provided for fewer classes, a limitation on entries and production records in most classes. The prospects of fewer classes and a limitation on entries were distasteful to many exhibitors, particularly those with large herds but there seemed to be unanimous support for the reintroduction of production records as a condition of entry.

At the 1922 show the offering for Holsteins was substantially higher than that offered for any of the other breeds. As years passed this imbalance became greater, and a committee was appointed in 1957, under the chairmanship of the author of this history, to review the situation. After doing so the members recommended a formula similar to that proposed for beef cattle, namely that the Royal should establish a basic offering and offer to match the grants of the breed associations. The Executive Committee reacted favourably, establishing the basic offering for each breed at $2,500. The Holstein-Friesian Association of Canada, the largest and wealthiest organization affected by this decision, was in a position to make a substantial grant, which accounts for the fact that the offering for Holsteins is still greater than that of the other breeds.

During the past 20 years many beautiful trophies have been donated to the Royal for perpetual competition in the dairy cattle division. In several instances the donations were made to perpetuate the memory of men who had been prominent exhibitors or active members of the committee. Among the renowned live stock breeders of the past whose memories are being perpetuated in this way are: R. R. Ness, J. H. Black and J. L. Stansell, Ayrshire breeders; Howard Corning and Jack Fraser, Guernsey breeders; Hon. George S. Henry, R. M. Holtby, M. L. McCarthy and Haley & Lee, Holstein breeders, and D. O. Bull, John Bull, W. Redelmeier, and Alfred Bagg, Jersey breeders. The trophies are fitting reminders of the contribution which these men made to breed improvement.

The Premier Breeder and Premier Exhibitor awards were established in 1937. These awards are made to the breeder and exhibitor winning the greatest number of points with animals which he has bred or exhibited. Although the banners which are awarded to the winners have little intrinsic value they are greatly prized. To win a Premier Breeder or Premier Exhibitor award at the Royal is tantamount to being declared the outstanding breeder, or the owner of the best herd of a particular breed, in Canada. The practice of issuing these awards, which originated with the dairy breeds, has been extended to other classes of live stock.

Aside from anything that has occurred in the show ring, the most significant development in dairy cattle production in the past 44 years has been the introduction of artificial insemination. "A.I." has revolutionized the industry. Actually it did not make much impact until the decade following its introduction. By that time two Holstein bulls, Montvic Rag Apple Sovereign and Montvic Rag Apple Marksman, had established enviable reputations. Not only were they outstanding show bulls in their own right, but each was siring offspring capable of producing large quantities of milk and of winning top honours in the show ring.

It is doubtful if two bulls have exerted a greater influence on a breed. A.I. made it possible for them to sire hundreds of offspring annually. For years a high percentage of the winners at the Royal were closely related to one or other of these great sires. As a result dairy cattle breeders began to comprehend the possibilities of A.I. and the program expanded at a phenomenal rate. In 1965, more than 60 per cent of all Holstein calves registered were the result of artificial matings. During the same year a record number were sold for export, presumably because foreign buyers recognized the excellence of Canadian Holsteins.

In considering developments over almost a half-century, it is interesting to recall that the founders of the Royal estimated they would need accommodation for 600 dairy cattle. Obviously they did not envisage such an increase in the dairy cattle population as has taken place. On several occasions the entries in Holsteins alone have approached the 600 mark, while the combined entry in the four dairy breeds has frequently exceeded twice that figure.

Along with the increase in numbers, there has been a striking turn-over in breeders and exhibitors. Most of the breeders who were prominent in 1922 have fallen victims to Father Time. However, at least four names are still very familiar in the Royal's dairy cattle division. Representatives of these four herds have been shown at all, or practically all, of the Royals held to date: J. W. Innes (Holsteins); R. R. Ness & Sons (Ayrshires); Alfred Bagg & Sons (Jerseys), and B. H. Bull & Sons (Jerseys).

The J. W. Innes herd which made Holstein history for many years is being carried on by the son of the founder, Gordon Innes, the member of the Ontario Legislature for the County of Oxford. Douglas Ness, an active member of the R. R. Ness & Sons firm in 1922, is the principal member of the original firm. Norman and Don Bagg are carrying on in the tradition of their father, and since his death have continued to win many of the top prizes in Jerseys.

Perhaps no herd of any breed in the entire fair has won more prizes and world-wide renown that that of B. H. Bull & Sons. In the pre-war years Duncan, or D.O. as he was generally called, shared the honours of breeding and showing outstanding animals with his brother Bartley. Following the war, D.O.'s son John became the active member of the firm. In addition John served on the Executive Committee following the death of his father. When John passed away in 1965, leaving a young family, it was feared that the herd might be dispersed. However it is intact under the original name, and chances are that, within a few years, a member of another generation of the Bull family will become head of the firm and a regular exhibitor at the Royal.

The years have produced a new group of exhibitors and the calibre of the cattle has continued to improve, due in no small measure to the fact that the industry was built on a solid foundation.

SWINE

Breeding Swine

During World War 1 Canada supplied enormous quantities of bacon to Great Britain but because the emphasis was on quantity and not quality, Canadian bacon got a bad reputation. After the war both sales and prices dropped. When the full impact of this dwindling British market became apparent in Canada a national swine conference was called. One of the results of this conference was that Canadian swine breeders thereafter concentrated on producing an ideal bacon-type hog, and the live-grading system was introduced.

These developments took place about the time the first Royal was held. Since the Royal was designed to be a leader in the promotion of meat animals of the type best suited to the Canadian market, hogs of bacon type were featured in the classification. In 1922, most hogs were produced in Eastern Canada. Five breeds were quite prominent: Yorkshire, Berkshire, Tamworth, Chester White and Duroc Jersey. A few other breeds, particularly the Poland China, were being raised in southwestern Ontario. The Royal provided separate classes for hogs of the five prominent breeds and a class for hogs of any other breed.

It is interesting to note that, in the year of the first Royal, Prof. H. Barton of Macdonald College, Que., summed up the prospects of the current swine breeds this way:

"The answer to the swine breed question of today is: Yorkshires and Tamworths are wise selections; Berkshires have possibilities; Chesters are doubtful market products; Durocs or Polands are a mistake; Hampshires are just novelties, and the Large Blacks are unnecessary."

Under the original classification, classes were offered as follows:

Boar, 15 months and over.
Boar, 9 months and under 15 months.
Bar, 6 months and under 9 months.
Boar, under 6 months.

A similar age division applied to the female classes.

In addition, there were group classes for senior herd, junior herd and get of sire.

After the introduction of grading, packers began to pay premiums for hogs qualifying for the top grades and to discount those in the lower grades. The adoption of this policy signalized the beginning of a trend — foreseen by Prof. Barton — which eventually led to the disappearance from Canada of Chester Whites, Duroc Jerseys and Poland Chinas. Although classes for these breeds were provided for a number of years, it soon became apparent that the Royal was encouraging the production of breeds that did not conform to bacon type. Consequently classes for the three fat hog breeds were discontinued in 1931.

During the early years of World War II, hog grading was replaced by carcass grading. Under this system the superiority of the Yorkshire and the weaknesses of the Tamworth and Berkshire were exposed and the Yorkshire became the dominant breed. By 1943 and for several years thereafter, more than 90 per cent of the hogs registered annually in Canada were Yorkshires.

Shortly after the war a number of Landrace herds were established, largely from stock imported from the United States or Great Britain. Although the Landrace is the national breed of Denmark, no Danish breeding stock has entered Canada, partly because of restrictions imposed under Federal Health of Animals regulations, and partly because of a reluctance on the part of the Danes to sell breeding stock to potential competitors in the world's bacon markets, although undoubtedly, a number of Landrace herds were established by Canadians who were under the impression that they were buying stock of Danish blood lines. Regardless of their origins, the number of Landrace herds continued to increase and the Royal added a classification for the breed in 1957.

In the meantime, scientists, on the staff of the Experimental Station at Lacombe, Alberta, were diligently engaged in the development of a new breed of swine. Berkshires, Chester Whites and Landrace were used as parent stock. These breeds were crossed in accordance with a pre-determined plan, following which the herd was closed and line breeding was practised for several generations. When type and other important characteristics had been stabilized the new breed was given the name "Lacombe" in recognition of the station at which it was developed. Breeding stock was sold to the public in lots, each comprised of one boar and three gilts. Thus many herds were established. By 1961 there were enough Lacombes in Canada to warrant the establishment of a classification for them at the Royal.

By 1964, the interest in Berkshires had declined to the point where the breed no longer had much economic significance in Canada. Accordingly the classification for the breed was eliminated.

Two developments of the early 1950's are worth mentioning — the establishment of a Breeder-Market Class and the introduction of a system of subsidizing the prize winnings of swine with certain record of performance qualifications. The Breeder-Market Class called for the showing of a boar, a gilt and a market hog from the same litter. The groups are shown alive, and then the market hogs are slaughtered. The final awards are based on a combined live and carcass appraisal. Although this class has been open to all breeds, Yorkshires have dominated the competition.

Before 1966, performance records were not a requirement in determining eligibility for showing. In 1951, however, supplementary prize money was offered for the prize winning progeny of animals that qualified under the Record of Performance Policy. In 1966, performance records became a condition of entry in certain classes and the practice of paying supplementary prizes was discontinued.

Committee Chairmen

The Royal has been fortunate in its choice of chairmen for the Swine Committee. Mr. R. W. Wade, Director of the Ontario Live Stock Branch and Secretary of the Canadian Swine Breeders' Association was the first Chairman. In 1925, he was succeeded by Mr. J. E. Brethour of Burford, the man generally credited with being the founder of the Yorkshire breed in Canada, who served up until the war. When the fair was resumed after the war, P. J. McEwen of Wyoming, Ont., a veteran Berkshire breeder, became the Chairman. Mr. McEwen served as a director of the Royal for 35 years, from 1922 to 1957 and was appointed an honourary director in 1958. He was followed by Dr. R. J. Pinkney of Cooksville, who held the office from 1949 until 1953. Since then no person has been Chairman for more than three years. The office has been held by G. B. Crow, a Yorkshire breeder; C. B. Boynton, a Tamworth breeder, Gordon Schweitzer, Joe Featherston and George Robson, all Yorkshire breeders.

In recognition of his many years of faithful service as Secretary, the Canadian Swine Breeders' Association donated the R. W. Wade Memorial trophy in 1954, to be awarded annually to the exhibitor of the first prize Yorkshire senior herd.

None of the veteran breeders of the first Royal is still exhibiting at the show. Perhaps this is not surprising. After all, 45 years have elapsed between these two fairs. However, it does seem unusual that only one of the originals was represented in the 1967 far even by a son or grandson. The lone exception was Hugh Hart, who showed Landrace in 1967, and whose father, Jim Hart, exhibited Tamworths in 1922.

Market Swine

At the first Royal the functions of the Breeding Swine and Market Swine Committee were performed by one committee under the chairmanship of Mr. R. W. Wade. Three years later a separate committee was established for each division and Mr. F. C. Fletcher was first Chairman of the Market Swine Committee. This Committee continued to function until 1952 when market live stock became the responsibility of the Market Live Stock Committee. Mr. E. S. Manning had the distinction of being the first chairman of this new committee. Aside from Mr. Fletcher, the only Chairman of the Market Swine Committee was Mr. S. E. Todd.

At the first fair there were classes for single barrows, pens of three, pens of five, and pens of ten. In addition, there was a class for a pen of seven feeder pigs weighing between 90 and 120 pounds. Actually this class was discontinued the following year, presumably because it was considered inadvisable for exhibitors to take home young pigs that had been exposed to infections.

In 1927, when the new swine barn became available, the classification was revised. Under the new classification there were classes for three barrows and five barrows or gilts, with both classes being open to pure breds, grades or cross-breds. In addition, there were classes for three barrows of each of the following breeds: Yorkshires, Berkshires and Tamworths. The class for ten barrows was replaced by an Inter-provincial Carlot Class which called for 40 barrows. For several years, competition in this class was quite keen with Ontario and Manitoba usually being strong contenders for top honours. When the fair resumed following the war carcass grading was the accepted practice. Consequently there did not appear to be any justification for reviving this class.

It is rather interesting to trace the weight ranges for market hogs established during the pre-war years. At the first show the preferred weights were 170 to 210 pounds. In 1923, the top limit was increased by 10 pounds to 220 pounds. By 1925, apparently 170 pounds was considered too light for a good market hog and so the minimum weight was increased to 180 pounds. At the same time the maximum weight was raised to 230 pounds, and a range of 180-230 pounds was continued until after the war.

During the Depression of the early 1930's, in an effort to stimulate trade, Canada and Great Britain signed an agreement under which Canada was granted a guaranteed market for specific quantities of agricultural products, but particularly bacon and cheese. Since this trade agreement provided an opportunity for expanding hog production, producers could foresee a ray of hope in the midst of despair. Accordingly, a concerted effort was made to increase hog production and improve the quality of the product.

To encourage better quality, Mr. J. Sainsbury, head of one of the largest British bacon importing firms, offered a trophy, to be awarded to the exhibitor of the best Wiltshire side. For the benefit of those not familiar with the term, a Wiltshire side is one side of a hog carcass from which the head, feet and backbone have been removed. At that time practically all pork products shipped from Canada to Britain were processed in this form. This trophy had to be won three times in order to become the property of an exhibitor. Mr. J. E. Brethour had the unique distinction of winning it in 1934, 1935 and 1936, the first three years it was offered. He generously offered to donate the trophy for perpetual competition in 1937. Since then it has been known as the Brethour trophy.

During the post-war years, Canada's bacon exports to Britain declined sharply. Within five years practically all surplus pork products were being marketed in the United States in the form of carcasses or cuts. In view of this development, there did not appear to be any logical reason for continuing to stage a class for Wiltshire sides. Hence, a change was made in 1955, when the Brethour trophy was offered for the best carcass from a pure bred hog, with the hog to be selected from a litter nominated in advance of the fair.

Earlier, the Canadian Meat Packers Council donated a challenge trophy to perpetuate the memory of Mr. S. E. Todd, a man who had served as secretary-manager of that organization for many years, and exerted a profound influence on the live stock industry. This trophy is awarded to the exhibitor of the champion carcass from a pure bred, grade or cross-bred hog.

There have been few significant developments in the market swine division during the past ten years. Worthy of mention, however, is the fact that, in response to consumer demand for leaner pork, the maximum weight for market hogs has been reduced to 210 pounds.

Because the Landrace and Lacombe breeds were introduced into Canada comparatively recently, supporters of these breeds have been inclined to feel that their pigs were being discriminated against in Interbreed classes. Indeed, Yorkshires continue to outnumber pigs of other breeds in the market classes by a wide margin. In 1965, an attempt to correct this imbalance was made by establishing classes for lop-eared pigs — which include the Landrace and Lacombes — and for erect-eared pigs. This change resulted in a better representation of the various breeds in the market hog classes.

Undoubtedly the three men who played the most important roles in guiding the destinies of the swine division of the Royal during the pre-war period were R. W. Wade, J. E. Brethour, and S. E. Todd. It is significant that a trophy has been donated to perpetuate the memories of each of these outstanding men.

SHEEP

Breeding Sheep

In 1922, sheep production constituted an important division of the Canadian live stock industry. In the years following, the sheep population declined at an alarming rate and reached an all-time low for the present century in 1965. During the early stages of the decline, per capita lamb consumption dropped. Following the war, however, it started to move in the other direction, ostensibly because lamb was the favourite meat of many of Canada's new citizens. To meet this demand large quantities of lamb are now imported annually.

Despite these production tends, the sheep division experienced fewer changes than any other division of the fair. Before the first fair, the committee adopted a classification which, with one minor change, is still in effect. Under that classification there were classes for yearling rams, yearling ewes, ram lambs and ewe lambs, and two group classes: one for a flock comprised of one ram, two yearling ewes and two ewe lambs; the other for a group of four lambs, bred and owned by the exhibitor. In 1930, a class for ram, two years old and over, was added, that being the only signicant change in the classification in 43 years.

At the first show, classes were provided for ten breeds: Lincolns, Cotswolds, Leicesters, Suffolks, Oxfords, Hampshires, Cheviots, Shropshires, Southdowns and Dorsets. In 1956, classes were added for North Country Cheviots and Corriedales, two breeds that attained considerable popularity after the war. By 1962, interest in Lincolns and Cotswolds had declined to the point where very few flocks remained in Canada. Since they are quite similar in many respects, the two breeds were combined for classification purposes.

Regardless of the changes in the industry, sheep breeders have proven themselves to be dedicated to their business. Several who exhibited at the first Royal are still active in the show ring. Among the veterans still participating are Fred Gurney and John Kelsey with Shropshires, and Charlie Shore with Cotswolds. In many other cases descendants of exhibitors at the first Royal are showing regularly. Included in this category are: Lloyd and Boyd Ayre, twin sons of Alf Ayre; Ephriam Snell, a son of James Snell; John and George Lee, sons of Herb Lee; Jim Bell, a son of David Bell; Everett Mark, a son of George Mark, and Harold Skinner, a son of Levi Skinner.

Breeders prominent at the first show who died childless or whose families did not carry on in the tradition of their fathers, were: A. & W. Whitelaw of Guelph; J. W. Springstead & Sons of Caistor Centre; Cecil Stobbs of Wheatley; John D. Larkin of Queenstown; Telfer Bros. of Paris; Peter Arkell & Sons of Teeswater; and R. J. Fleming of Toronto.

An exception to this rule is Dave McEwen of London, whose father, Col. Robert McEwen, was a charter member of the Royal and an important exhibitor for many years. Although Dave is still an active commercial sheep breeder, he seldom competes at shows.

Incidentally, Col. McEwen was the first Chairman of the Sheep Committee and continued to serve in that capacity until 1937 when he was succeeded by Mr. George L. Telfer. Following the war, David E. McEwen became Chairman, the first occasion in the history of the Royal that a father and son held the same office. Dave continued to serve until 1951. Since then no chairman has held office for more than three years. They were: J. H. Willmott of Milton; Wilfred Shields of Caistor Centre; Ernest Redelmeier of Richmond Hill; Keith Henderson of Guelph; W. H. J. Tisdale of Oakville and Lloyd Ayre of Bowmanville.

Market Lambs
Anyone whose knowledge of the market lamb classes is limited to the past 10 years is likely to be surprised at the classification adopted in 1922. At the first fair, there were classes for wether lambs, under one-year of age sired by a long-wooled ram, and for lambs of a similar age, sired by a short-wooled ram. There were classes for pens of three whethers, over one-year and under two-years of age, sired by long and short-wooled rams. Finally, there were classes for pens of ten lambs, under 90 pounds, and for pens of ten lambs 90-100 pounds.

In 1922, there was a fair demand for mutton. In many cases it was the product of old sheep. However, good mutton was obtained from wethers one to two years of age. Because of the variation in the quality of this product, mutton soon began to lose favour with the public. Sensing this trend, all classes for market wethers, over one-year of age, were dropped in 1927. During that year the new sheep barn was completed. With more accommodation available, the classification was revised. In the revision several of the group classes were consolidated and an inter-provincial carlot class was added. This class called for 25 lambs. Unfortunately, it never attracted many entries, so was dropped in 1932 for lack of competition.

Coincidental with the dropping of the class for yearlings, classes were established for pens of three market lambs weighing 90-120 pounds, and 120 pounds and over. Under this classification it was possible for representatives of all breeds to participate in the competition. However, as the demand for smaller cuts of meat increased, the classes for heavy lambs were eliminated, and a maximum of 110 pounds became effective in 1950.

Mr. F. C. Fletcher, whose name is intimately associated with many divisions of the fair, was the first chairman of the Market Live Stock Committee. In 1929, he was succeeded by Mr. S. E. Todd, who occupied the position until 1947. Upon retirement of Mr. Todd, Mr. Fletcher was reappointed, and he carried on until the division became a part of the Market Live Stock Committee in 1952.

Wool

Classes for the fine grades of wool most commonly produced in Canada, were established at the first fair. Three years later classes for fine wool with fairly long staple, such as that produced by Ramboulet and Corriedale sheep, were added. Since then, the changes in classification have been consistent with those in the grading regulations of the Canada Department of Agriculture.

In an effort to focus attention on wool, classes were established, in 1928, for the shearling rams of each breed carrying the best fleeces. Approximately one-half of the total prize money was contributed by the Canadian Co-operative Wool Growers. Apparently these classes did not have much appeal. In any event they were dropped after two years.

The only other significant development, in connection with the wool division, took place in 1956, with the introduction of the International Sheep Shearing Competition. Contestants are required to shear two sheep and awards are determined on: shearing time; manner of handling sheep; absence of second cuts in the fleece; and wool preparation. The Sunbeam Corporation (Canada) Limited has co-operated by furnishing the shearing equipment and has donated a valuable trophy for perpetual competition. Since the competition was initiated, the contestants have been equally divided between Canada and the United States, with most of the winners being Americans.

GOATS

No provision was made for the showing of goats until 1952. In that year an abbreviated classification was provided and a representative of the Milking Goat Society was named to the Breeding Sheep Committee. Classes were provided for: doe, in milk; doe, one-year and under two, not in milk; and doe under one year, of the Saanen and Toggenburg breeds. In addition, a class was offered for Nubian doe, any age.

In the years following, the Nubian breed has been elevated to the same status as the other two breeds, and two extra classes for each breed have been added. Generally speaking, the goat classes have seldom attracted more than two or three exhibitors per breed.

Sales of market live stock have been a feature of every Royal Agricultural Winter Fair. In the early years a few sales of breeding stock were featured as well. The first one mentioned in the records was held in 1924 under the auspices of the Dominion Shorthorn Association. At that sale 20 females and 11 bulls averaged $247.25 and $258.60 respectively. In the same year the Grand Champion Steer with a weight of 1,260 pounds brought $1.60 per pound, or a total of $2,016.00 — almost as much as eight bulls.

These sales of breeding stock had a rather sporadic history until the late 40's. Tom Hays, who had come out of the West to establish a thriving export business in live stock, and particularly in cattle, proposed to the breed associations and to the Executive Committee of the Royal that he be permitted to hold consignment sales of outstanding cattle during the fair. The members of the Royal Executive approved the proposal and a satisfactory financial arrangement was reached. Even so, the breed associations were somewhat reticent. Finally, in 1949, the Canadian Aberdeen Angus Association agreed to co-operate in the holding of a sale which proved to be the forerunner of the Sales of Stars. At that sale 37 head of Aberdeen Angus cattle sold for an average price of $706.00.

Prompted by the success of this sale the other beef breed associations consented to participate the following year. At the 1950 sales, 34 Aberdeen Angus sold for an average of $1,259; 32 Shorthorns averaged $828, and 25 Herefords averaged $1,092.

In 1951, the Ayrshire Breeders Association of Canada joined the group. Other associations to become co-sponsors of sales were the Canadian Jersey Cattle Club and the Dual Purpose Shorthorn Club, both in 1952; the Holstein-Friesian Association of Canada in 1953; the Canadian Sheep Breeders Association in 1957, and the Canadian Guernsey Association in 1965.

By the middle 50's interest in some of the sales was beginning to wane. The first to be discontinued was the Dual Purpose Shorthorn sale. It was held for the last time in 1957. The Aberdeen Angus, Shorthorn and Hereford sales were not held after 1960.

Several factors contributed to the decline in interest in these particular sales. Perhaps most important was the fact that breeders were reluctant to consign their best cattle. Furthermore some consigners were inclined to indulge in by-bidding either directly or through the medium of a third party. Realizing the situation, many potential buyers withdrew their support, with the result that there were several unsold cattle at every sale.

Despite a few disappointments these sales have been an important factor in stimulating Canada's export trade, since many of the animals are purchased by breeders from outside Canada. Seldom has a year passed without some cattle being sold to buyers from Mexico, Argentina and other South American countries, and to Italy. U.S. buyers have always been prominent at the sales. In 1965, a few head of Holsteins were sold to buyers from France — probably the first time Canadian cattle ever were sold to France.

In addition to stimulating exports, these sales have established prices that every breeder strives to attain. In Aberdeen Angus the top price was obtained in the 1950 sale when a heifer from the herd of Edwards Bros. of Watford, Ont. was bought by Marydale Farm of St. Francesville, Louisiana, for $8,350. In Shorthorns, the honour of receiving top price went to Grant Campbell of Moffat, Ont., who received $8,000 for an animal purchased by George Cox of Grand Fork, N.D. The Hereford top price was received by W. A. Crawford-Frost of Nanton, Alta., at the 1950 sale, for a bull bought by Carman C. Lyons of Wallacetown, Ont., for $5,000.

A great many five-figure prices have been attained at Holstein sales, but the record was established in 1958 when a bull calf consigned by H. J. Wilcox and Sons of Beeton, Ont., sold for $30,000 to the Ontario Association of Artificial Breeders. The top price for Jerseys was obtained the same year when H. I. Mais of St. Andrews, N.B., paid $5,000 for a three-year-old cow consigned by B. H. Bull & Sons of Brampton, Ont. No spectacular prices have been received for Ayrshires, the top price being paid in 1951 when S. C. Oland of Halifax, bought a heifer from the consignment of R. O. Biggs of Dundas for $2,300.

A new North American record for a consignment sale was established in the 1965 Holstein Sale of Stars when 26 head sold for an average of $3,270. The top price of $15,200 was paid by Roy Ormiston of Brooklin, Ont., for a six-year-old cow consigned by Ebydale Farm of Kitchener, Ont. Second highest price in the sale was paid by Adelfa C. De Ortiz of Mexico who purchased the grand champion cow of the show for $10,000.

POULTRY AND AGRICULTURAL PRODUCTS

The Bonanza boys, modelled in butter

Alex Cameron with his
Champion goose

Judging White
Plymouth Rocks

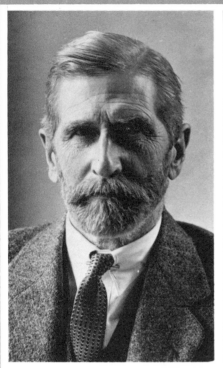

LEFT: J. Lockie Wilson, member of the original Seed Crops Committee

RIGHT: The Wheat Trophy

R. Keegan and A. G. O. Whiteside judging seed

Presentation of the
Barley Trophy by
J. R. Cross and
J. A. Northey

Lady Eaton, long-time
supporter of the
Flower Show, with
Lt. Gov. McCurdy
of Nova Scotia

Biggest cheese made in
Canada in 50 years
was this 1700-pounder

CENTRE: The Rye Trophy

RIGHT: Holland's display
of fruit and
vegetables, 1948

Barbara Ann Scott
with Lady Eaton's
display, 1950

Adam and Eve and
the apple display

Roses form the centre-
piece in this overall
view of the Flower Show

CHAPTER 4 Poultry and Agricultural Products

DURING the past 50 years poultry production has undergone more dramatic changes than any other branch of agriculture. At the time the first Royal was held most farmers maintained flocks of hens. The "egg money," by immemorial tradition, was spent by the farm wife on groceries and household necessities. In the fall, these farmers had a number of roasting chickens to sell and the revenue from this source was ear-marked for the purchase of Christmas presents for the family.

The breeds most common then were Plymouth Rocks, Rhode Island Reds and Wyandottes. These were general-purpose breeds. The hens could lay a reasonable number of eggs and the cockerels developed into excellent roasting chickens. Although Leghorns were better layers, they were not such good eating.

In 1922, chicken was a delicacy — something you served only on special occasions. The politician's promise to put "a chicken in every pot" was a seductive vote-getter. Turkey was a real luxury, enjoyed by the affluent at Thanksgiving and Christmas. Generally speaking, turkeys were raised in small flocks which were allowed to roam during the summer and fall months, frequently being forced to live on the food they could find. As the Christmas season approached they were penned and fattened up. Ducks and geese were raised by a few farmers, usually those who had streams or ponds near their farm buildings. Ducks and geese also had to be good scavengers in order to survive.

Actually there were few significant changes in poultry-raising until after the war. In the meantime, however, scientists had

been busy developing hybrid strains of chickens, capable of producing more eggs than birds of the standard breeds. In poultry
meat production, hybrids were also being used. In that field, the
objective was to produce the most chicken in the shortest time
with the least feed. By perseverence, poultrymen finally succeeded in producing three-pound fryers or "broilers" in 11 to 12
weeks.

With the development of hybrid strains, some producers
began specializing in egg production, others in meat production.
In either case there was a trend towards larger flocks and these
large flocks soon became the dominant factor in the industry. At
the same time, the small family flock began to disappear (along
with the "egg money") and soon flocks of less than 500 birds were
practically non-existent. Those specializing in meat production
marketed their birds as broilers, thereby making chicken available at all seasons of the year. The increase in broiler production
was accompanied by a sharp decline in the production of roasting
chickens.

In turkey production the development of the broad-breasted
bird ranks as a major achievement. The discovery of antibiotics
capable of controlling common turkey diseases dispelled the
theory that it was necessary to raise birds on range. Soon specialists began rearing turkeys in large numbers in confinement. By
applying scientific techniques they were able to reduce costs of
production substantially, and these reductions were passed along
to consumers. Within a few years, turkey and chicken ceased to
be luxury items.

The changes in the poultry show were less dramatic than
those occurring in production. At the first show there were classes
for every breed that had an economic significance in Canada.
Many of the largest breeders exhibited at that show and at the
ones held during the next 15 years. In addition to chickens there
were classes for ducks, geese, turkeys, pigeons, rabbits and cavies.
The poultry exhibit occupied the entire upper floor of the East
Annex. It was not uncommon to have on display 8,000 to 10,000
birds, and the Royal Poultry Show became recognized as the
largest in North America. A great many specialty clubs, such as
the American Bantam Associations, the American Rose Comb
White Leghorn Club, and the Canadian Barred Rock Club, held
their championship shows at the Royal. Not only did these championship shows help to swell the numbers on exhibit, but they
served to attract the best birds being produced on this continent.

By 1946, the evolution which was taking place in the industry began to have an impact on the production of standard poultry. Many of the old breeders switched to commercial production and replaced their flocks with hybrid strains. Exhibits in the standard poultry classes declined sharply and in 1957 the classification was carefully screened and classes for breeds that had ceased to have much economic significance were eliminated. By 1960, there was more space available in the upper East Annex than was needed for poultry. Because there was a keen demand for this space for other purposes, the poultry exhibit was transferred to the pavilion, a large area connected to the upper West Annex by a passageway. Following this move the emphasis was placed on quality. Although entries declined to 3,000, many of the birds were potential champions.

J. S. Greenshields of Hamilton was the first Chairman of the Poultry Committee and deserves a great deal of credit for getting the show started on a solid basis. However, the man who guided its destinies during the period when the poultry show experienced its greatest popularity was J. A. Northey, who had the honour of serving as President of the Royal in 1947 and 1948. Other committee chairmen who displayed a talent for leadership were: Harry Bickle (1947-51); Wallace Clancy (1952-60); Joe T. Robb (1961-63); and R. S. (Dick) Nicholls (1964-66).

In the light of the changes that have taken place in poultry production, many have questioned the wisdom of continuing the poultry show. Admittedly, standard poultry does not appear to have any place in a modern, commercial operation based on high-producing hybrid strains. However, it must be borne in mind that standard poultry are essential to the development of hybrids and good hybrids stem from good standard parent stock. By encouraging the production of high quality standard poultry, the Royal is making a worthwhile contribution to the poultry industry.

FIELD CROPS

Fifty years ago farmers used to feed what they grew and grow what they fed. A farmer kept just as much livestock as he could feed with grain and other crops that he could grow on the home farm. Some farmers still work that way but most of them are buying more and more of their grain requirements, and keeping a much greater number of animals than farmers did at the time of the first Royal. Even so, live stock men are still very much concerned about increasing their crop yields.

It is generally agreed that good seed is the key to good crops. The founders of the Royal recognized this fact and by establishing a Seed Division. The first few seed shows were fairly small compared with those held in later years but, in some respects, they were more practical.

In 1922, classes were provided for a limited number of varieties of grain, clover and grass seeds, and potatoes. At that time the most popular varieties of winter wheat were Dawson's Golden Chaff and O.A.C. 104. In oats, Alaska, Banner and O.A.C. 72 dominated the list. Although these varieties no longer occupy the spotlight, they were used extensively by plant breeders in the development of new varieties. As new varieties became recognized, competitive classes for them were provided.

In potato production, the tendency has been to reduce the number of varieties. At the first Royal, potatoes were classified into three main groups: Green Mountain, which included the late-maturing varieties; Irish Cobblers, the early maturing varieties; and New Yorker, the varieties that were classed as intermediate from the standpoint of maturity. Although the system of grouping still prevails, most of the varieties for which classes were provided in 1922 have passed out of existence.

Old timers will undoubtedly recall some of the familiar names of 45 years ago. Included in the Green Mountain were: Bethel Beauty, Blightless Wonder, Carmen, Delaware, Farmer, Freeman, Gold Coin, Gurney's White Harvest, Keystone, Long Island Wonder, Norcross, State of Maine, Uncle Sam, and White Mountain.

The early varieties for which classes were provided included: Early Dixie, Early Eureka, Early Petoskey, Early Standard, Early Vickton, Flourball, Potentate and Bells Deposit.

In the New Yorker group were such varieties as: Dooley, Carmen No. 3, Arcadia, Great Divide, Jackson White, Late Vickton, Lily White, Million Dollar, Noxall, White Giant, White Swan and Russet.

Nowadays, the most common varieties are Sebago, Katahdin, Chippewa, Cherokee, Irish Cobbler, and Netted Gem. Undoubtedly, many of the varieties exhibited at the first Royal were used in their development.

Classes for sheaves of grain were featured at the first Royal.

The men who exhibited in these classes were real artists, and the sheaves they created added greatly to the attractiveness of the seed show. Although classes for sheaves are still provided, few entries are received. Presumably – like so many other agricultural skills – sheaf-making has become a lost art.

Auction sales of seed were staged at the fairs held during the early 20's. Exhibitors in the open classes were required to send more than a tiny sample of their seed. They had to submit two bushels of grain or, in the case of clover, grass seed or seed potatoes, one bushel. In addition there were commercial classes in which exhibitors were required to show quantities ranging from 10 bushels in the case of potatoes, to 20 bushels in the case of wheat. During the latter days of the show, all exhibits in both the open and commercial classes were sold by auction. These sales allowed the Royal to play an important role in the distribution of good seed.

In 1924, however, the quantities comprising exhibits in this division were reduced by half and further reductions were authorized a few years later. As the quantities were reduced, the possibilities of holding successful sales diminished and they were eventually eliminated. Nevertheless, they did serve a useful and practical purpose for many years.

Originally the small seed section was limited to classes for red clover, sweet clover, alsike, alfalfa, and timothy. At that time sweet clover was very highly regarded, both as a feed for cattle and as a soil-building crop. However, as new species were developed, it lost much of its popularity. Among the new species to obtain a high rating are: Birdsfoot Trefoil, Brome Grass, Orchard Grass, and the Fescues, all of which are now eligible to compete.

In the early 30's, when farmers were desperate because of shrinking markets and low prices, any type of production that showed promise of providing extra income was eagerly sought. With the prospect of changes in Ontario's liquor laws, particularly as they pertained to beer, the brewing industry was anxious to encourage the production of barley suitable for malting. Consequently, barley competitions were organized on a county or district basis in Ontario and Quebec, with the local winners being eligible to compete at the Royal for generous cash prizes donated by the Brewers' Association. Mr. Donald L. Scott, a prominent seed grower in the Ottawa valley, who died suddenly while still a comparatively young man, had the distinction of winning this special class in each of the first three years in which it was offered.

By 1937, the scope of this division had expanded to the point where it was re-named the Seed and Grain Division. As new classes were added, the name began to grow to an unmanageable length. In 1951 classes for hay were added, and the name was changed to the Seed, Grain and Hay Division. When classes were provided for Leaf Tobacco in 1958, it became the Seed, Grain, Hay and Tobacco Division. By the following year it had become the Seed, Grain, Hay, Tobacco and Christmas Tree Division. At this point, a halt was called to the burgeoning nomenclature and someone had the bright idea of calling it the Field Crops Division, and that is how it is still known.

In the meantime there were a number of significant developments. One related to the establishment of a 50-bushel winter wheat competition. Like the malting barley competition, this one was organized on a county basis, with Maple Leaf Mills Limited being the co-sponsors. The purpose of the competition was to stimulate the production of wheat crops that yielded 50 bushels per acre or more. Only contestants who achieved that goal and whose samples of wheat had won top prizes at local shows were eligible to compete at the Royal for prizes donated by Maple Leaf Mills Limited.

Perhaps the most significant, and certainly the most dramatic, development took place in 1947 when three companies donated magnificent "world championship" trophies. Quaker Oats of Canada Limited donated the trophy for oats; the Canadian National Railways, the one for wheat, and the Brewers' Association of Canada Limited, the one for barley.

In the years following, other trophies equally as attractive, were donated by Parrish and Heimbecker Limited, for rye; Maple Leaf Mills Limited, for corn; Victory Soya Mills Limited, for soy beans; the Canadian Seed Trade Association, for forage crop seeds; the Cockshutt Farm Equipment Limited, for hay; the Imperial Leaf Tobacco Company of Canada Limited, for tobacco, and the Searle Grain Company Limited, for flax. In addition, a trophy to be offered as an international award for seed potatoes was donated by the Canadian Horticultural Council.

Undoubtedly, the prospects of winning one of these trophies has been an important factor in stimulating international competition in the Field Crops Division. Since they were first offered, entries have been received from every province of Canada, except Newfoundland, from many states in the United States, from England, Scotland, Northern Ireland, France, Sweden, South Africa, French Morocco, Tanganyika, New Zealand, South Africa and Kenya.

Since these trophies have become available, those offered for competition for crops most widely grown in Canada, have been won as follows:

		Number of trophy winners			
RESIDENCE OF THE WINNER	WHEAT	OATS	BARLEY	RYE	FORAGE SEEDS
Alberta	14	11	10	6	3
Saskatchewan	1	1	3	2	—
Manitoba	—	5	—	—	—
Quebec	—	—	—	—	2
Ontario	1	—	3	6	3
B.C.	2	—	—	—	3
England	1	—	3	4	4
Scotland	—	2	—	—	—

Another important development took place in 1964 when a section for pedigreed seed was added to the classification. Exhibits in this section are drawn from sealed bags on the premises of exhibitors by officers of the Canada Department of Agriculture. Thus, the sample shown is truly representative of seed that the grower has for sale.

Throughout the years the Seed Committee has been well balanced, being comprised of growers, representatives of the trade, and officials of the Field Crops Division of the various Departments of Agriculture. The government representatives have played an important part in the success of this division by encouraging the best growers in the country to exhibit. Entries from other countries have been received, in many cases, as a result of approaches made by members of Canada's Foreign Trade Service.

J. Lockie Wilson, Director of Agricultural and Horticultural

Societies for Ontario, was the first chairman of the committee and continued to serve in that capacity until 1936. His successor was W. T. G. Wiener, Secretary of the Canadian Seed Growers' Association, who held the post until 1949. Since then no person has been chairman for more than three years. In recent years the office has been held by: J. W. Mackay of Ottawa; A. H. Martin, Toronto; N. D. McKenzie, Toronto; W. E. Breckon, Burlington; Frank Marritt, Keswick; L. B. Mehlenbacher, Cayuga; F. W. Presant, Toronto; D. L. Parks, Toronto, and Alex McKinney, Brampton.

THE FLOWER SHOW

When the first Royal was held the flower show was relegated to a position on the upper floor of the West Annex along with the fruit and vegetables. A year later, however, it was moved to the ground floor, a position it has occupied ever since. In that location it is seen by everyone who attends the fair, and all are charmed by its beauty.

Originally, the flower show was strictly competitive. There were classes for roses, chrysanthemums, pompons, and carnations. In the years following, the classification was expanded to include classes for potted plants, such as cyclamen, begonias, and African violets. Throughout the entire period, roses and chrysanthemums have occupied the spotlight, the other exhibits being arranged to harmonize with them.

For many years the principal exhibitors in the competitive classes were green house operators and retail florists, each intent on impressing the public with the merits of his products. With the passing of time, however, the number of green house operators declined and there was a sharp reduction in the number of exhibitors.

Unlike exhibits in other divisions of the Royal, cut flowers have no salvage value when the show is over. To compensate for this loss the cut flower exhibitor receives any prize money he may win and any future sales which might result from contacts made at the show. Unfortunately, the public puts a high premium on the first prize and there is little advertising value in finishing in second place. Since there is only one first prize in each class, a lot of potential exhibitors, fully aware of the public attitude, are reluctant to hazard their prestige.

For these, and perhaps other reasons, there was a sharp decline in the number of exhibitors during the 1930's. In order to maintain the size and beauty of the show, it became necessary to switch from competitive to display exhibits, particularly in the rose section. Accordingly, the Royal entered into an arrangement with the Rose Society, under which the society would be remunerated for sponsoring the rose display. Each year, the society has adopted a different arrangement, and has been most ingenious in coming up with new and striking displays.

During the post-war period some unique and attractive arrangements were employed. On one occasion, a small ferris wheel was used as the main prop. The roses, which bedecked the seats, showed off to advantage as the wheel rotated. On another occasion, a giant swan mounted on glass, to create the illusion that it was swimming on water, was the central figure. The roses were mounted on the swan's back and arranged around the borders of the simulated pond.

Unfortunately, roses don't retain their beauty long at room temperature and the display must be replaced about half-way through the show. Of course, this adds to the cost of the rose exhibit. However, the extra expenditure has proven a sound investment, because of the important role played by the Flower Show in general and the rose show in particular in attracting lovers of beauty to the Royal.

Smaller flower displays have always been featured at the Royal, usually around the perimeter of the flower show area. The most consistent exhibitors of these displays have been Lady Eaton, the Department of Parks and Recreation, and the Niagara Parks Commission. In the early years of the Royal, the Central Experimental Farm at Ottawa, Sheridan Nurseries, and several other nurseries, sponsored display exhibits. Invariably, these displays were comprised of flowering plants, foliage plants, beautiful cut flowers artistically arranged in a picturesque setting which included brooks, waterfalls, mill wheels and walking paths.

During several years the Toronto Garden Club took an active part in the flower show. Their exhibits featured shadow boxes which were used effectively to display various types of floral arrangements.

Exhibits sponsored by retail florists have added variety and beauty to the show. From the standpoint of originality of design they have been outstanding. In most years some florist has been able to apply his imagination by designing in flowers a subject, currently making headline news. One of the favourite subjects for many years was a Tiger Cat, symbolizing Hamilton's great football team.

In 1965, the Floriculture Committee sponsored a new feature, unique in North America. In co-operation with Interflora Incorporated, floral arrangers were brought to the Royal from England, France, Germany, Switzerland, Italy and Mexico. From a central stage in the centre of the rose display, banked with flowers, these artists demonstrated flower arrangements characteristic of their native countries.

Through the years the Royal flower show has received widespread acclaim. Undoubtedly, much of its success has been due to the support of companies, firms and individuals whose main objective has been to make the Royal Flower Show the finest in the world. It is impossible to make reference to all who have given unstintingly of their time and talents. However, without intending to slight anyone, a word of praise should be extended to the Dale Estates of Brampton, Toronto Department of Parks and Recreation, Niagara Parks Commission, Gardeners' and Florists' Association, Roses Incorporated, Toronto Women's Garden Club, Toronto Retail Florists Association, and last but by no means least, Lady Eaton.

The competitive aspect of the flower show is now on the wane and it will probably be necessary to buy the flowers that will be displayed in future shows. Even so, there will always be a need for people trained in the ancient art of floral arranging so that the characteristic beauty of the flowers may be displayed to the best advantage.

FRUIT AND VEGETABLES

In 1922, the fruit and vegetable exhibits were the responsibility of one committee. The first chairman was Mr. F. F. Reeves. Since then, two generations of the Reeves' family have been represented on the committee. In 1923, the committee was divided into two divisions, one with jurisdiction over fruit, and the other dealing with vegetables.

The history of the fruit show reflects the changes that have taken place in the industry during the past 45 years. At the first fair, there were 53 exhibitors, of which 16 were from British Columbia; 4 from New Brunswick; 1 from Quebec, and the rest from Ontario. During the next 10 years, the fruit show continued to attract exhibitors from those provinces and occasionally from Nova Scotia. About the middle of the 1930's, exhibits from provinces, other than Ontario, began to decline and no exhibits have been received from outside Ontario since the fair was resumed after World War II.

In the absence of entries from other provinces, and a decline in the number of Ontario exhibitors, a low point was reached in 1963, when only four growers exhibited. Despite the fact that each showed a fairly large number of apples and thereby contributed to a colourful display, it was quite apparent that interest in exhibiting was approaching the vanishing point. Accordingly, the Fruit Committee recommended that competitive classes be discontinued and that the apple section of the Ontario Fruit and Vegetable Association undertake to sponsor a large display designed to promote the sale of apples. From the standpoint of benefit to the industry, this proved to be a wise decision. The display exhibits have been very attractive. In addition, to stimulating the demand for apples, they have done much to enhance the appearance of the show.

A number of factors contributed to the decline in exhibitor participation. Originally exhibitors from outside Ontario were motivated by the prospect of developing Ontario markets for their products. For a while they achieved some success. However, apple-growing became a very depressed industry in the 1930's. Net returns declined, particularly to those who had to bear the expense of shipping long distances. As a result growers in other provinces started to look for markets elsewhere, and when they achieved some success in that connection, transferred their promotional activities to the areas which offered the best opportunities for making sales.

Undoubtedly the changes in classification were a factor too. At the first few fairs there were classes for varieties that are merely names to members of the younger generation. Included in the classification were such varieties as: Tolman Sweets, Wagner, Winesap, Fameuse, King, Baldwin, Jonathan, Newton, Stark, Ben Davis, Gravenstein, Golden Russet and Blenheim Pippin. Gradually, most of these varieties declined in popularity and, as the impact became apparent, classes for them were eliminated. This procedure continued until there were only three varieties left — McIntosh, Spies and Delicious.

When the first fair was held, city families used to buy apples by the barrel in the Fall and store them in their cellars for the Winter, and apples were shown at the Royal in barrels. Later, when trade with Britain developed, boxes became the standard container for showing apples, and continued to be as long as the competitive classes were maintained. Since the changeover was made a section of the exhibit area has been used to promote the practice of giving boxes of apples for Christmas.

Transcending all other reasons for the decline in exhibitor participation, however, has been the labour problem. There is something impractical about the showing of apples. The trees from which show apples are to be selected have to be carefully pruned, the young apples have to be thinned by hand so that those remaining will have a better chance to develop, the trees have to be sprayed with great regularity, the apples have to be hand-picked very carefully to avoid bruising, and finally, the apples which are to comprise the exhibit must be chosen with meticulous care for shape, size and colour. There are very few men trained for this work and most of them are too busy to be bothered with show business.

Developments in the vegetable division have followed a similar pattern. For obvious reasons, competition has been limited to those vegetables which are fresh in November, such as cabbage, cauliflower, carrots, onions, and celery or to root vegetables that can be stored, such as potatoes, turnips, beets and parsnips. Since fresh vegetables will not retain their fresh appearance for long when held at room temperature, exhibitors from outside Ontario are at a great disadvantage. Actually, even local growers have to make replacements from time to time throughout the show. Because of this situation, Ontario growers have always dominated the fresh vegetable exhibit. Nevertheless, growers from other provinces, particularly the Maritimes, Manitoba and Alberta, have been regular exhibitors in the potato classes.

In 1958, Salada-Shirriff-Horsey Limited donated a beautiful trophy to be awarded annually for the grand championship in table stock potatoes. Since it was first offered, the trophy has been won by growers in Alberta, Manitoba, Ontario, New Brunswick and Prince Edward Island. The only grower to win it more than once is Mrs. A. R. Chorney of East Selkirk, Man., who has the distinction of being a three-time winner.

Among the men who strove diligently to improve the fruit and vegetable exhibits in the pre-war period were: W. F. W. Fisher of Burlington; Percy W. Hodgetts, Director of the Ontario Fruit Branch; W. L. Smith of Burlington; Frank Palmer of Vineland Experimental Station; W. L. Hamilton of Collingwood; and G. H. Mitchell of Thornbury, Ont.

Although competition is the basic principle upon which most divisions of the show operates, it has outlived its usefulness in the fruit division and it is quite conceivable that competitive classes in the vegetable division may be discontinued in the near future. If this happens, chances are that vegetable growers will also adopt the display type of exhibiting.

Dairy Products
Competitive classes for butter and cheese were established at the first Royal and few changes have been made in the classifications. However, there has been a switching of emphasis from the large, round, 90-pound cheeses which were popular 40 years ago, and are still the standard unit in our export trade, to smaller, oblong cheeses.

For many years, exhibitors have been required to deliver their exhibits to a nearby cold storage warehouse where the judging takes place. Because of the lack of facilities for displaying an appreciable number of entries, only the top prize winners were brought to the Royal. In 1947, following the installation of permanent refrigerators in the area underneath the Coliseum seats, an entire section was allocated to the dairy products division. Since then, it has been possible to display a much higher percentage of the prize winners.

Competition in butter has always been maintained on a national basis with creameries in Alberta, Saskatchewan, Manitoba, and Ontario capturing top honours most frequently. Cheese production in Canada however is largely centred in Ontario and Quebec, and most of the cheese exhibits have originated in these provinces.

Since they are static exhibits, displays of butter and cheese failed to have much public appeal. In an attempt to add glamour to these exhibits, the Ontario Cream Producers' Association requested, in 1952, that space be provided for a butter sculpture. This request was granted and an artist was selected to sculpture the Hon. T. L. Kennedy, Minister of Agriculture for Ontario. It was an excellent likeness and created a great deal of interest. Many fair patrons, who might otherwise have given the dairy products exhibit a fleeting glance, spent a lot of time studying the sculptures. To add prestige to the area, the section in which the dairy products were exhibited was designated "Dairy Lane."

In the years following, a number of prominent men in public

life were sculptured in butter. Included in the group were: R. Hon. J. G. Gardiner, Minister of Agriculture for Canada; Hon. Leslie M. Frost, Premier of Ontario, and Marilyn Bell who swam across Lake Ontario and became Canada's athlete of the year in 1954. In the late 50's subjects, famous in fairy tales, such as Little Miss Muffet, and the Cow Jumped over the Moon were chosen. In more recent years, attention has been focussed on famous television personalities.

In 1964, dairy organizations celebrated the one hundredth aniversary of the founding of the first cheese factory in Canada. Established in Oxford County by Harvey Farrington, a native of New York State, this factory proved to be the forerunner of an important industry. Special reference to Mr. Farrington and his achievement was made in the 1964 cheese exhibit.

Poultry Products

The establishment of classes for dressed poultry were delayed until 1947, following the installation of permanent refrigerators. Classes were provided for chickens, ducks, geese and turkeys. Because of the many changes in the industry, the classification has been altered considerably during the past 20 years. Perhaps the most significant changes, however, have been in the chicken and turkey sections where the trend has been to market birds at lighter weights. There are now more classes for chicken and turkey broilers than ever before. As these classes increased, some classes were eliminated, particularly in sections for roasting chickens.

As in the case of dairy products, the dressed poultry show has been national in scope. However, the Western provinces and Ontario have been the most prominent prize winners. The emphasis has always been on quality rather than quantity. At one stage competition was restricted to birds qualifying for special grade. Inasmuch as birds of this grade carry a considerable amount of finish, in fact more than the public demands, the supply is limited and the number of entries declined accordingly. Consequently, to revive interest and maintain the show on a practical basis, the eligibility requirements were lowered to permit the showing of grade A birds as well as those qualifying for special grade.

Members of the provincial and federal Dairy and Poultry Departments have rendered valuable assistance in these two divisions. Being frequently in contact with members of the trade, they were in a position to play a leading role in obtaining entries.

The National Dairy Council, producer dairy organizations and the Poultry Products Institute have been helpful too, particularly in sponsoring display exhibits designed to promote the use of dairy and poultry products.

Honey and Maple Products

Before the opening of the first Royal, the Ontario Beekeepers' Association petitioned for the establishment of competitive classes for honey. The directors, who weren't sure that such classes would attract many entries, rejected the request. However, they did agree to make a grant of $300 to the Beekeepers' Association, on the understanding that the money would be used to finance a comprehensive display of honey.

This practice was continued until 1926 when an inter-provincial competition was started. Provincial Departments of Agriculture or provincial beekeepers' associations were eligible to compete. Each exhibitor was allocated an area 10 feet by 12 feet in which he was required to display about 1,000 pounds of honey including light, amber and dark liquid honey, granulated, and comb honey.

Although substantial cash prizes were offered, the competition never attracted many entries. Consequently, it was replaced by competitive classes for individual producers in 1935. While the number of entries has never been large there have always been enough to make an attractive display. Furthermore, the show has been supported by producers from most provinces of Canada. The honey is sold at prices slightly above those prevailing on the market at the end of the show. Invariably, the demand has far exceeded the supply.

In 1953, this division was expanded to include classes for maple syrup and maple sugar. There were only 6 entries the first year but they have increased substantially since then. Competition has been dominated by producers from Quebec and Ontario, with Quebec producers winning most of the prizes.

Tropical Fish

Although not an agricultural product, tropical fish are a popular feature of the Royal. At one time the tropical fish were included in the flower show, but entries increased to the point where they were given a separate division.

Throughout the years the tropical fish show has been operated by committees, made up of people intensely interested in this field. Classes are provided for practically every known variety. School children have been encouraged to take an interest in this division by the offer of a special prize for the best community tank exhibited by an elementary school.

Fish, as a matter of fact, were one of the outstanding attractions of the first Royal. Patrons were invited to come and see "the famous sextet of walking perch owned by George Wright of the Walker House." These fish, said to be "the only three pairs in existence" were put through their paces by Prof. James Palmer, superintendent of the Walker House Aquarium. They somehow managed to walk along a special platform, using their fins for legs, then flipped themselves into a tank. They were supposed to be natives of India and Egypt and were on the point of becoming extinct despite the fact that they had been known to "walk" 18 miles to a new water hole when the old one dried up.

JUNIOR ACTIVITIES, SPECIAL FEATURES

Chairing the winners
of the Queen's Guineas

The Fashion Show

Judging the Queen's
Guineas

A. J. Casson and Sidney
Watson judging the
Poster Competition

The Cat Show

Tropical Fish Exhibit

4H Clubs come from
all across Canada
and parts of the U.S.
to participate
in the Royal

CHAPTER 5 Junior Activities, Special Features

F ROM the outset the directors of the Royal recognized the importance of encouraging youth to take part in the fair and have always sponsored a full program for young people. At the first Royal there was a steer-feeding competition, open to boys and girls, 10 to 18 years of age. In 1923, the second and last time this competition was held, the first prize steer was declared the Grand Champion of the show. It was shown by Raymond Clarkson of Weston, who is now farming in the Brampton district where he breeds Holstein cattle and Suffolk sheep. The steer sold for $1.55 per pound.

In 1924, the original competition was replaced by an Inter-County Baby Beef Contest for young men, under 30 years of age who had taken part in local contests conducted under the direction of the Department of Agriculture. In 1933, the contest was made more restrictive by limiting competition to boys aged 14 to 20. Otherwise there were no significant changes in the rules governing the contest in the pre-war years.

During the war the Baby Beef Club program expanded at a remarkable rate in Ontario. Girls were admitted to membership and joined local clubs in large numbers. When the Royal was resumed in 1946, provision was made for the top calves in the local clubs to be shown in a special class and sold by auction on the final day of the fair. At the suggestion of the Hon. T. L. Kennedy, Minister of Agriculture for Ontario, this class was designated the "King's Guineas" class.

The designation "King's Guineas" has a special significance. About the middle of the last century, Edward, Prince of Wales, later King Edward VII created a fund to be used in the development of agriculture in Upper Canada and placed it in trust with the Agricultural and Arts Society. A few years later this society was dissolved and the fund was transferred to the Ontario Department of Agriculture to be kept in trust in perpetuity. The proceeds were to be disbursed at the discretion of Ontario's Minister of Agriculture. Consequently, the King's Guineas, which became the Queen's Guineas when the present sovereign ascended the throne, are provided from this fund.

Competition in this class has always been keen, presumably because of the spectacular prices received for many of the champion steers. When John Kinsman received $5.50 per pound for his 1946 champion, the problem of getting boys and girls to participate in the boys and girls beef club program was solved. However, this was just a forerunner to some of the high prices paid in later years.

An all-time high of $10.50 per pound was received by Kenneth McKinnon of Hillsburgh, Ontario in 1947. When this young man won the championship again in 1948, the rules were changed to exclude the winner of a championship from further competition.

Other young people who have got high prices for their steers are: Shirley Early (1961), $7.00 a pound; Ronald Storey (1962) $9.00 a pound; Sandra Peart (1963) $8.25 a pound; Boyd Nelson (1964) $9.00 a pound; and Bert Tupling (1965) $8.50 a pound. All "Guineas" champions have been bought by Loblaw Groceterias Limited or Dominion Stores Limited. (The names of the winners and the prices received are listed in the Appendix.)

It is rather ironical that very few of the top winners, in fact a relatively small number of the exhibitors, have continued to show at the Royal after graduating from their 4-H status. One notable exception is Miss Earley, now Mrs. Jerry Miller of Bowling Green, Ohio, who returned in 1967 to assist her husband in showing the Reserve Grand Champion steer of the show.

Although the Guineas classes have received the greatest amount of publicity, they have been only a small part of the total program for juniors. In the 1930's, when heavy draught horses were at the peak of their popularity, foal clubs were about as numerous as calf clubs. As a grand finale to the club program, a foal club competition was staged at the Royal. Although competition was restricted to the best foals from local clubs, classes of 50 or more were not uncommon. The Hon. T. L. Kennedy donated a trophy for horsemanship, the winner being the boy who accumulated the greatest number of points in the foal and showmanship classes. By 1946 tractors had replaced horses on many farms, interest in horse breeding was definitely on the wane, and the foal club competition was not renewed in the post-war years.

A section for members of Boys' and Girls' Grain Clubs was established in the Field Crops Division in 1934. Under the original classification, classes were provided for Hard Spring Wheat, Durum Wheat, Early Oats, Six-Rowed Barley and Green Mountain and Irish Cobbler Potatoes. As the club program expanded, classes for additional varieties were added to the classification. Winning exhibits in the junior section have always been eligible to compete for world championship awards, and, as a matter of fact, several junior exhibitors have won world titles:

Wheat	Rickey Sharpe	Alberta	1950
Wheat	Howard Roppel	Alberta	1951
Wheat	Ronald Leonhardt	Alberta	1952
Wheat	Miss Gail Adams	Alberta	1958
Wheat	Laurence Gibson	Alberta	1964
Wheat	Larry C. Hixt	Alberta	1965
Oats	Myron D. Zacharko	Alberta	1962
Potatoes	Miss Ann MacAuley	P.E.I.	1962

Live Stock Judging competitions have been traditional with the Royal. At the 1922 fair, there were two competitions — one for junior farmers, the other for college students. Teams from Ontario, Manitoba and Alberta participated in the first college competition. A few years later, however, colleges in other provinces withdrew their support, probably because of the high costs involved. The requirements were then lowered to let teams from agricultural schools within a reasonable distance of Toronto, seldom have more than three teams competed. On the other hand, interest in the Inter-County Competition has always been quite keen.

Some very attractive trophies are offered in this competition. The Jeffrey Bull Memorial trophy, donated by B. H. Bull & Sons to perpetuate the memory of a member of the firm who was killed in action in World War I, is awarded to the winning team. In 1926, following the death of Mr. E. H. Stonehouse, a prominent dairyman and a charter member of the Royal, the National Dairy Council donated a trophy in his memory, to be awarded to the contestant winning the highest number of points in the judging of dairy cattle. In the same year the horsemen of Canada donated a trophy to perpetuate the memory of Robert Graham, one of Canada's greatest breeders, exhibitors and judges of horses. This trophy is awarded annually to the top contestant in horse judging. Of all the trophies and other awards donated since the war, perhaps the most coveted is the F. K. Morrow Scholarship. The winner receives a sum of money to be used towards his tuition fee and expenses while taking a two-year course at an agricultural school of his choosing.

In 1928, largely through the courtesy of the Canadian National Railways and the Canadian Pacific Railway, the two top winners in each provincial calf and swine club competition were given an all-expense trip to the Royal. While at the show they were required to participate in an Inter-Provincial Live Stock Judging Competition, with the winners in each division being declared the national champions.

Three years later, the Canadian Council of Boys' and Girls' Clubs was organized and this organization then assumed responsibility for conducting the Inter-Provincial Club competitions. Under its guidance the program was expanded to include competitions in all club projects.

Following the war, some members of the Council began to promote the idea of adopting the 4-H label, which at that time was recognized in many countries, but particularly in the United States. Some of the founders objected on the grounds that such action would result in the Canadian program losing its identity. In 1959, however, after several years of heated debate, the advocates of the 4-H designation won their point and the name of the organization was changed to the Canadian Council on 4-H Clubs. Following this change, the judging competitions were discontinued. Instead, the provincial champions were given trips to Toronto and Ottawa, where they had the opportunity of visiting many points of interest, including a day at the Royal.

Another highlight in the junior program was the "500 party." Organized in 1927 by the Ontario government, 10 boys from each county and district who had achieved distinction in local judging competitions were awarded trips to the Royal. In 1930, the program was expanded to include girls, increasing the size of the party to 500. This program was continued until 1938, but was not revived after the war.

In 1951, the T. Eaton Company announced an Eaton Agricultural Scholarship award open to boys who had not yet reached their 23rd birthday. The scholarship provided for all college fees, lodging and board for a four-year course in agriculture at a Canadian institution, chosen by the winner. Each provincial minister of Agriculture was required to select a candidate from his province. The boys chosen attended the Royal at the expense of the T. Eaton Company, and while there were interviewed by a special committee charged with the responsibility of choosing the winner. This scholarship award was discontinued in 1958. During the years that it was offered, however, winners were selected from Alberta, Saskatchewan, Ontario, British Columbia, Quebec and Prince Edward Island.

In addition to providing an opportunity for juniors to participate in competitions and programs, members of the younger generation have been privileged to sit on the Board of Directors of the Royal. When the class of '05 graduated from the Ontario Agricultural College at Guelph, the members established a scholarship for the outstanding member of the junior year. In 1947, the constitution of the Royal was amended to permit the winner of this scholarship to become a director of the Royal. Furthermore, the Junior Farmers Association of Ontario is entitled to be represented on the Board by two directors. Many of those who were associated with the Royal as juniors have become its strongest supporters.

The directors of the Royal, conscious of their responsibility to young farmers of this country, have developed programs to encourage them to produce better live stock and agricultural products and to improve their knowledge in these fields. They are also conscious, however, of a responsibility to the urban youth. School children have been encouraged to attend the fair, particularly as members of organized groups. Every year thousands attend and most of the children are given assignments by their teachers. In the search for answers the children obtain a great deal of practical information about Canada's basic industry.

Included in the thousands of children of public and secondary school age who attend are hundreds of students from the Ontario College of Art who take advantage of the opportunity to improve their skills in drawing and painting. Specimens of their work has been included in this volume.

FOX, MINK, DOG AND CAT SHOWS

During the early 1920's, fox furs were the height of fashion. To meet the ever increasing demand, fox breeding developed into an important industry in some provinces, but particularly in Prince Edward Island. Under the circumstances, it was quite natural that a fox show would be staged at the Royal. The first one, held in 1923, attracted 30 exhibitors who showed 353 foxes. Of this number 266 were exhibited by breeders from Prince Edward Island. There were classes for black or extra black, dark silver, medium silver and extra pale silver. The exhibit of live foxes was complemented by a display of pelts.

At this show the foxes were exhibited in the lower West Annex. Unfortunately, foxes have a distinct smell. Ladies and gentlemen attending the Horse Show nearby, who were happy to follow the foxes on horseback across country fields, were reluctant to encounter the odoriferous little animals at such close quarters. Consequently, the foxes were hounded into the Upper West Annex and their former dens were filled with the flower show's fragrant blooms which were deemed to be more compatible neighbours for the occupants of the Horse Show boxes.

Fox entries were considerably higher in 1924 and continued to increase in the years following. In fact the increase was so great that many had to be refused for lack of accommodation. A futurity class, sponsored by the Fox Breeders' Gazette, helped to stimulate interest in the show. Breeders intending to compete in this class were required to nominate the sires and dams in June and to select their exhibits at show time for these matings.

Although the fox show was generally considered to be a division of the Royal, the actual operations were under the direction of the Canadian Silver Fox Breeders' Association and the Association put up the money to cover most of the prizes. As the number of exhibits increased, the association became more demanding, insisting that additional space be allocated and that the Royal make a larger contribution to the prize money. By the end of the decade, tension developed between the officials of the two organizations. Because of the growth which was taking place in many divisions of the show, the Royal could not give the fox exhibit any more space. The breeders were having their problems, too. Fashion is fickle and fox fur was unaccountably going out of style again. The association's revenue was falling fast and there was less money to spare for prizes. Unable to resolve their problems, officials of the two organizations decided to discontinue the fox show in 1930.

During the Depression, the trade in such luxury items as fur coats, was somewhat less than brisk. When money became more available again, people were switching to mink. In 1937, the Ontario Fox Breeders' Association persuaded officials of the Royal to revive the fox show but despite a fairly successful exhibit it was apparent that fox fur for the time being at least, had had its day. The 1937 show was the last fox show at the Royal.

After the war, people were talking about "status symbols" and the symbol of the highest status was a mink coat. Mink breeders asked for a show at the Royal and their request was granted in 1954. At the first show 655 mink were exhibited by 39 breeders from Ontario, Manitoba and British Columbia. In the next two years entries increased as breeders from other provinces, notably Prince Edward Island and New Brunswick came in. Despite the increased interest on the part of exhibitors, the directors of the sponsoring organization began to hedge on the payment of prize money grants and so the mink show was discontinued after operating for three years.

In 1923, officials of the National Kennel Club pressed for the holding of a dog show. Although no action was taken that year, their request received favourable consideration the following year. Since the directors of the Royal didn't know much about running dog shows they entered into an agreement with the National Kennel Club, under which full responsibility for the operation would be placed in the hands of a Mr. Foley of Philadelphia, who knew all about dog shows. Mr. Foley was to pay all expenses, including the prize money. In return, he was to get all receipts from general admissions to the dog show. Unfortunately, the agreement was not completed until late in the year, and the show didn't attract as many exhibits or spectators as expected. Disappointed with the results, the directors of the National Kennel Club decided to hold their show elsewhere during the next two years.

In 1927, however, they reversed this decision and succeeded in making arrangements for holding a dog show at the Royal. Officials of the club were to operate the show. Revenue from admission fees was to be divided, 75 per cent to the sponsors and 25 per cent to the Royal. Between 1927 and 1938, a number of successful dog shows were held. Every effort was made to obtain the services of the best judges in America. Confident that they would receive fair treatment, breeders in Canada and the United States supported the show whole-heartedly and entries often had to be refused because of lack of accommodation. This problem was partly solved in 1931 with the completion of the Horse

Palace. The pavilion, which forms part of the Horse Palace, was an ideal location. In addition to being larger than the space formerly used it had fewer entrances and exits, making it easier to control the crowds. In several years just before the war the paid attendance exceeded 10,000.

When the Royal was re-opened after the war, the dog show was continued. In 1947, however, the Canadian Kennel Club adopted a ruling under which no dog show could operate for more than one day. Naturally the directors of the Royal were not interested in reserving a large space, for which there were many requests, for a one-day show. Although they would have been allowed to hold one-day shows on several successive days, this idea was not very appealing, either. There was a lot of bickering between officials of the two organizations and finally the arrangement was cancelled. In 1953, the dog show was revived, but it was far from successful. Since then, the subject has been discussed several times, but to date the Royal has been obliged to veto all proposals because of a lack of suitable accommodation.

Several cat shows have been held, just before or just after a dog or fox show and in the same location. Decisions about holding cat shows have been dependent on whether or not space was available.

The first cat show was held in 1929 under the auspices of the Royal Canadian Cat Club. Between then and the outbreak of war, a number of cat shows were held, but seldom in two successive years. As was the case with dog shows, the Royal played the role of landlord by providing the space while the sponsoring organization assumed responsibility for operating the show.

SPECIAL FEATURES

The founders of the Royal envisaged a show which, except for the Horse Show, would be strictly agricultural and which would be staged mainly for the benefit of a rural audience. However, the directors soon discovered that a lot of money is needed to run a show of the size of the Royal. Furthermore, it was forcefully impressed on them that a considerable amount of this money must come from general admissions.

From the outset the revenue from the Horse Show was up to their expectations. On the other hand, the income from general admission was somewhat disappointing. It soon became apparent that the fair would have to offer a more diversified program, if more people were to be attracted through the front doors.

In an effort to increase attendance from across Canada, provincial days were established in 1928. Each of the eight days was given a distinct designation. For example, the opening day was Canada day; the others were: British Columbia, Maritimes, Quebec, Ontario, Manitoba, Saskatchewan and Alberta days. On the day that a province was being honoured, prominent people from that province were invited to occupy seats in the President's Box during the Horse Show. The prize-winning live stock from the province were paraded during the evening performance and the provincial Minister of Agriculture, or someone designated by him, undertook to comment on the live-stock industry of the province while the animals passed in review.

This was an interesting feature for a few years. The railway companies entered into the spirit of the program and organized special train tours to the Royal. Men and women in Western costumes became a common sight at the fair. During this period the federal minister of agriculture was host at a dinner, usually held on the evening of opening day. At these dinners it was customary to include in the menu, dishes that had a distinctive provincial connection, such as: Prince Edward Island potatoes, British Columbia apples, Alberta beef, and Ontario cheese. When the effects of the Depression began to be felt, these banquets were discontinued. By that time people from other provinces couldn't afford to make the trip to the Royal and the provincial days had lost much of the glamour. The practice came to an end, and the Royal had to turn to other attractions to build the crowds.

In 1927 the Royal had become host to the National Horse Shoe Pitching Contest, conducted under the auspices of the Ontario Athletic Commission. In the first year, 140 teams competed. These contests attracted a great deal of attention and helped boost the attendance during the 10 years they were held. No contests were held after the war but, in 1954, the sport was revived under local auspices. However, horseshoe-pitching, like quilting bees and taffy pulls, seemed to have run its course as a wholesome rural pastime. In any case, without the excitement of a national championship at stake, horseshoe-pitching failed as a spectator sport and was soon discontinued.

Canada Packers Limited has always been a strong supporter of the Royal. The company has always bought most of the market live stock offered in the auctions. Keen bidding by the company's buyers has resulted in premium prices for all live stock offered for sale. In 1952, Canada Packers extended its support of the Royal by sponsoring a national square dance competition which was quite popular and continued for another two years.

In 1955, and the two years following, the company undertook to sponsor a cooking school. Demonstrations were presented several times a day in a theatre in the Upper East Annex.

In 1958, Canada Packers decided that it was time for another change, and agreed to sponsor the "Children's Royal," one of the most popular attractions ever staged at the Royal and it continued until 1965. Unlike the regular live stock exhibit, the Children's Royal featured mother animals with their young — a cow and her calf, a sow with her litter of pigs, and so on. The exhibit was arranged with great imagination and attracted peoples of all ages, but particularly city children, many of whom had never seen baby animals before.

During the late 50's, the Wool Bureau of Canada cooperated with the Royal by sponsoring fashion shows which were staged several times a day. The garments featured in these demonstrations were created by Canadian designers and made from Canadian wool. Adjoining the theatre in which the demonstrations were held were the entries in the fleece wool classes and an exhibit sponsored by the Ontario Association of Spinners and Weavers. Thus, the cycle was complete. First, the natural wool, then demonstrations showing wool being spun into yarn and yarn being woven into cloth, and finally, the finished garment made from wool.

When the Wool Bureau decided to withdraw from the field, fashion shows were staged on special platforms erected in the flower court. Co-sponsors were the Canadian Mink Breeders' Association, The Retail Furriers' Guild of Canada, and the Toronto Dress Manufacturers Guild. Of course, mink garments were featured. Staged in this beautiful setting, banked with flowers, with models parading to soft organ music, the fashion shows were most impressive. During this period, a number of popular c.b.c. radio shows originated from the same stage.

Two competitions, started in the 1950's, have been popular attractions. Entries in the International Photographic Competition, first held in 1953, have been increasing with each passing year. In 1965, 4,366 pictures were submitted by 1,114 contestants from about 30 different countries, including some behind the Iron Curtain. The various entries are screened by a committee and only the best are displayed at the Royal. Since the inception of this competition, the Toronto Camera Club has made a valuable contribution to its success.

The other competition, started in 1959, is for fair posters. It is divided into three categories: Posters related to agricultural shows; posters for horse shows, and posters for agricultural products. Many attractive posters are entered by organizations in all parts of the world, particularly Europe.

In 1963, representatives of six commodity groups were invited to share in a food project which became known as the Farm Food Fair. Those accepting the invitations were: Dairy Foods Service Bureau; Ontario Beef Improvement Association; Ontario Fruit and Vegetable Growers' Association; Ontario Hog Producers' Association; Ontario Wheat Producers' Marketing Board, and the Poultry Products Institute of Canada. The Ontario Hydro acted as co-sponsor and Hydro home economists demonstrated unusual ways of preparing and serving dishes made from Canadian farm products.

These are a few of the special features that have been staged at various times to broaden spectator interest in the Royal. As the farm population has declined, it has become increasingly apparent that such features must become an integral part of the daily program if attendance is to be maintained at a high level. Furthermore, none of these features can be classified strictly as entertainment. In fact, most of them have had an important educational value.

THE CANADIAN AGRICULTURAL HALL OF FAME ASSOCIATION

During the 1959 Chicago International Live Stock Exhibition, Prof. George Raithby of the Ontario Agricultural College, Harold White, Secretary-Manager of the Canadian Shorthorn Association, and the writer who, at that time, was Live Stock Commissioner for Ontario, met by chance in the Saddle and Sirloin Club. This world famous Club is decorated with the portraits of many outstanding agriculturists, past and present. The three of us spent some time in studying the portraits and in recalling the achievements of many of the individuals, particularly those whom we had known personally. Finally, the suggestion arose that steps should be taken to establish a similar club or portrait gallery in Canada.

That casual remark which at the time sounded more like wishful thinking than a realistic approach to the subject, prompted the formation of the Canadian Agricultural Hall of Fame. The proposal was later discussed with agricultural organizations in Ontario and members of the Executive Committee of the Royal. Everyone approached seemed to think that it was an excellent idea, and pledged his moral support. A meeting was held in 1960, at which a temporary committee was named and authorized to draft a constitution and by-laws.

Under the constitution which was approved, provision was made for the affairs of the Association to be conducted by a Board of 12 directors, three of whom are to be from Western Canada, three from Quebec and the Maritimes, and the remaining six from any part of Canada. Any person engaged in agriculture, directly or indirectly, is eligible for membership upon payment of a fee of $25. Agricultural organizations are also eligible for membership, at a fee of $100. All fees are for life and no annual dues are levied.

The organization is incorporated under the Companies Act of Ontario in the name, "The Canadian Agricultural Hall of Fame Association." Its primary object is to recognize people who have made an outstanding contribution to Canadian agriculture.

At the outset it was agreed that only deceased persons should be recognized during the first few years and that such persons should be honoured by having their portraits hung in a gallery to be erected at some future date. Each member was granted the privilege of making one nomination annually, on the understanding that he would assume responsibility for the cost of the portrait in the event that the nomination was approved.

The Association began its work in 1961. Fourteen nominations received that year were approved by the portrait committee. Although the Association still had no suitable gallery in which to hang the portraits, 28 were accepted in the following year. However, when the front of the Coliseum was remodelled in 1963, a unique chapel-like structure was erected at the entrance to serve as The Canadian Agricultural Hall of Fame. The 42 portraits received in 1961 and 1962 were transferred to this building, and the 16 received in 1963 were added. When all were in place it was obvious that the Association could not continue to accept portraits annually in unlimited numbers. Consequently, at the 1963 annual meeting, the directors were empowered to approve a maximum of five nominations in 1964. This number was further reduced, in 1965, when a maximum of three was established.

Thus, during the first five years of operations, the portraits of 63 men and three women were hung in the Canadian Agricultural Hall of Fame. Included in this distinguished group are people from every province of Canada, except Newfoundland. A great many were prominent in the breeding of live stock. Among the others are the founder of the Women's Institutes, former leaders of farm organizations and of the farm press, specialists in seed production, agriculturists, and men who made a great impact on agriculture while serving in the political field.

Although The Canadian Agricultural Hall of Fame and the Royal Agricultural Winter Fair are separate organizations, they are closely allied. Since the Hall of Fame Association was formed, the general manager of the Royal has served as its secretary. The portraits presented each year are accepted at an official ceremony held during the Royal, and thousands of those attending the Royal make a special point of visiting the portrait gallery.

To date, the portraits of deceased persons only have been accepted. It is expected, however, that this policy will be changed in the near future, and that people who are making an outstanding contribution to agriculture will be appropriately honoured during their active careers.

CENTENNIAL YEAR

Canadians in all walks of life experienced a sense of pride as they shared in the glamour of the various functions that were held to commemorate the one hundredth anniversary of their country's birth. Although EXPO '67 occupied the spotlight throughout a six-month period, the 39th Royal Agricultural Winter Fair proved to be a fitting climax to the activities of a year dominated by spectacular events.

The 1967 Royal was a truly "Royal" Show, one in which the various events were staged in a dramatic but dignified fashion. Actually the pattern was established on the two days previous to the opening when delegates from eleven member societies, operating on four continents, met in the Royal York Hotel for the biennial conference of the Royal Agricultural Society of the Commonwealth. Membership in this organization, formed in 1957 at the instigation of His Royal Highness The Prince Philip, Duke of Edinburgh, is restricted to societies within the Commonwealth that have been granted permission to include the word "Royal" in their titles. Hence the Royal Agricultural Winter Fair is the only Canadian member.

Prince Philip, the first and only president of the Society, attended the conference and delivered the keynote address. Other speakers from United Kingdom, and from Australia and Canada presented papers dealing with various phases of the conference theme which was "Agricultural Engineering." On the closing night of the conference Mr. and Mrs. John A. McDougald were host and hostess at a dinner given in honour of the delegates and attended by leaders in governments, the directors of the Royal and their wives.

On the opening day of the fair His Royal Highness, accompanied by fair officials, made a tour of inspection of the exhibits. In recognition of centennial year the buildings were attractively decorated, an improvement in decor which did not go unnoticed by our distinguished guest. Throughout the tour, he displayed a keen interest in the exhibits, inspecting them carefully and stopping frequently to chat with exhibitors. He was particularly impressed by the Royal Food Show, the first one of its kind to be held in Canada, and graciously obliged those in charge by delivering a short address to mark the opening of the show.

During the evening he rode into the Coliseum, accompanied by Mr. McDougald, the President of the fair, in a George IV phaeton drawn by two matched teams of Hackneys, hitched tandem and ridden by postillions. After circling the arena the phaeton was stopped in front of the Royal box, the occupants alighted, Prince Philip inspected the Guard of Honour, and then delivered the following address:

Ladies and gentlemen: Few countries owe so much to agriculture and to their farmers as Canada. This is worth remembering at all times but in this the 100th year of Confederation and here at the Royal Agricultural Winter Fair, it seems a most appropriate time and place to pay a generous tribute to Canadian farmers.

The early settlers were pioneers in more ways than one. To leave home and to face unknown hazards required considerable courage and much faith. To survive the back-breaking labour and the hardships of life the year round demanded physical and moral stamina of a high order. But not content with that they designed and built machinery and equipment which their particular conditions demanded. And, of course, when they had the time, they enjoyed the traditional country sports and especially anything to do with horses.

These things they did for themselves and for their families but very soon they became responsible for Canada's growing prosperity. The export of their surplus production made it possible for the modern industrial Canadian nation to emerge and to prosper.

The drive and the energy which brought these early farmers success both for themselves and for their country has continued ever since. Their descendents have built great cities and thriving communities. But all the time the farmers have tried to improve their own performance, through shows like this and competitions, co-operative schemes, colleges and research laboratories and many other means, they have searched for a better method, more knowledge and greater productivity.

And as a climax, they got together from every province of the Confederation and organized the Royal Agricultural Winter Fair. So tonight we salute the farmers of Canada, backbone of the nation and food producers to the world. And now it's time for the show to begin. Ladies and Gentlemen, the 39th annual Royal Agricultural Winter Fair is open.

To commemorate Canada's one hundredth birthday, special centennial medals were offered in the competitive classes for live stock, agricultural products and horse show events. Bearing the Royal Agricultural Winter Fair crest on the one side and the centennial symbol on the other, the medals were awarded to the winners of grand championships.

Also recognized at the fair were men who have exhibited at every fair held to date. Known as the "Old Guard," these men were presented with lifetime passes to the Royal at a special luncheon held during the fair. The veteran of the party, Mr. S. E. Griffin of Acton was born two years after Confederation. Others to be honoured were: T. Alex Edwards (beef cattle); F. W. Gurney (sheep); John R. Kelsey (sheep); Dan Lerch (horses); Ralph McCall (poultry); Douglas Ness (dairy cattle); Russell Parker (beef cattle); Charles J. Shore (sheep); and William Sinclair (field crops).

Several months previous to the opening of the fair, General Dwight D. Eisenhower, G.C.B., O.M., of the United States Army, accepted an invitation to officiate at the closing. Unfortunately, shortly before the date scheduled for his arrival, he was forced to cancel the engagement on advice of his physician. In his absence Mr. McDougall read his message, the contents of which are as follows:

> It is with deep regret that I have to tell you of my inability to be present as you announce the close of Toronto's Royal Agricultural Winter Fair. Because the doctors have scheduled for me a physical examination for this weekend, and which will require close medical supervision for some days in advance, I must remain in the immediate vicinity for the period. In the hope that I might be with you I have waited to the last moment before sending this message but am now compelled to do so. My disappointment is all the greater because of my profound respect and affection for Canada and its people and because of the personal compliment implicit in your invitation. Finally, on my behalf, will you please make the announcement that the Fair is hereby officially closed? Please convey to all present an expression of these sentiments and extend to them my warm greetings and best wishes.
>
> Sincerely
>
> DWIGHT D. EISENHOWER

Yes, 1967 was a historic year for Canada, but it was also a milestone in the life of the Royal Agricultural Winter Fair: one that will long be remembered by those who had the good fortune to attend.

PEOPLE

LEFT: Prof. George
E. Day

RIGHT: George Pepper

LEFT: D. C. Flatt

RIGHT: W. A. Dryden
(President 1919-23)

LEFT: C. F. (Bill) Bailey, first General Manager

RIGHT: E. M. Carroll, President, 1924-26

D. O. Bull, Charter Member and past President, 1927-29

LEFT: Alfred Rogers, 1930-31

RIGHT: Col. Harry McGee, 1932-35

Stewart G. Bennett
(left), 1953-54, with
Agriculture Minister
J. G. Gardiner and Fair
General Manager
C. S. McKee

Lt. Col. Stuart C. Bate
(right), 1955-56, with
Mrs. Bate and old-timer
Frank C. Fletcher

C. F. W. Burns, 1957-58,
with his son Michael

J. H. Crang, 1959-60, wins Premier Guernsey Breeder Award

George Rodanz (left), 1961-62, with the Earl of Feversham, inspects the guard

Brig. F. C. Wallace,
1963-64, with Agri-
culture Minister
Harry Hays, at closing
ceremonies

LEFT: Col. D. B. Weldon,
1965-66, with
Shorthorn Lassie

RIGHT: H. R. H. Prince
Philip with John A.
McDougald, 1967

Prince Philip chats
with young admirers

Prince Philip, with
the author, addressing
Royal Agricultural
Societies of the
Commonwealth

CHAPTER 6 People

No history of the Royal would be complete
without some reference to the men who have guided its destinies during nearly a half-century. The 18 men who occupied
the office of president served with distinction, each giving unstintingly of his time and talents in promoting the best interests
of the Association.

At the outset it was generally agreed that the president should
hold office for two years, but that under exceptional circumstances the term might be extended to three. It was also understood
that the presidency should alternate between members whose
main concern was both the agricultural or horse show aspects
of the Royal. The wisdom of these decisions has been amply
demonstrated by the fact that there has been no disposition on
the part of anyone associated with the fair to break with the
tradition.

As was pointed out in the opening chapters, a national fair,
which would serve as the show window for Canadian agriculture,
was the brainchild of W. A. Dryden. In addition to conceiving
the idea, Mr. Dryden had the distinction of casting the ballot
which decided the site of the fair. Under the circumstances, it
was only natural that he should be honoured by being elected
the first president of the Royal Agricultural Winter Fair.

Mr. Dryden's father, the Hon. John Dryden, was the first
Minister of Agriculture in the Province of Ontario, holding office
from 1890 until 1904. Will, as he was commonly known, inher-
ited Maple Shade Farm at Brooklin from his father. There he
developed one of the outstanding herds of Shorthorns in North

America. Although Shorthorns were his first love, he had a keen appreciation of all classes of live stock. He took an active part in many live stock organizations, serving as president of the Canadian Shorthorn Association, chairman of the Canadian National Live Stock Records, and chairman of the Board of Directors of the Canadian Cooperative Wool Growers Association.

During the decade previous to the opening of the Royal, most Ontario live stock associations and agricultural organizations held their annual meetings at the Carls-Rite Hotel, at the corner of Front and Simcoe Streets in Toronto. This historic old hotel, which has since been demolished, became recognized as the head-quarters for agricultural activities and a friendly relationship was established between members of the agricultural fraternity and the proprietor of the hotel, Mr. E. M. (Mac) Carroll. Undoubt-edly this mutual spirit of friendship caused Mr. Carroll to be-come an ardent booster of the Royal. Fortunately, he had many friends at City Hall too, and as a result was in a position to act as a liaison between the promoters of the Royal and their future landlords at a critical time in the Association's history. In recog-nition of his contribution to the Royal, Mac Carroll succeeded Will Dryden as president.

The third president was another of Canada's outstanding agriculturists. Mr. D. O. Bull, senior member of the firm B. H. Bull and Sons of Brampton, was known in all parts of the world where Jersey cattle were bred. Undoubtedly, he did more to promote this breed in Canada than any other man of his time. Incidentally, the portraits of Mr. Dryden and Mr. Bull are hang-ing in the Canadian Agricultural Hall of Fame, which in itself is a tribute to their outstanding achievements in the field of Canadian agriculture.

Mr. Bull was succeeded by Mr. Alfred Rogers, a well known Toronto industrialist and president of a coal company. Although primarily interested in the Horse Show, Mr. Rogers proved to be a good friend of the agriculturalists.

The next president, Mr. Harry McGee, was the first of a number of farmer-businessmen to be elected to the presidency of the Royal. In addition to being the owner of a farm and a successful breeder of Shorthorn cattle, Mr. McGee was vice-presi-dent of the T. Eaton Company. Incidentally, the Municipal Offices of the Toronto suburb of Etobicoke are on or very close to Mr. McGee's old farm.

Mr. Gordon F. Perry held the office of president longer than anyone else. First elected in 1936, he held office until 1946. However, no shows were held during seven of those years, because the buildings were occupied by the Armed Forces. Mr. Perry was a Toronto industrialist and a sportsman who was extremely interested in equestrian events.

His successor, Mr. J. A. Northey, became associated with the Royal as a member of the Poultry Committee. During the 1930's he bought a farm near the corner of Sheppard Avenue and Leslie Street, just north of Toronto, where he established a very fine Jersey herd. However the farm fell victim to the urban sprawl and is now the site of a large number of suburban homes. Aside from his farming activities, Mr. Northey was president of the Telfer Paper Box Company.

Before becoming president, Mr. John W. McKee served for many years on the Horse Show Administrative Committee, including one year as its chairman. As president, however, he made a point of becoming familiar with all divisions of the fair and as a result perceived that the Royal had outgrown the existing facilities. Subsequently he played a leading role in obtaining pledges of government support for the building program that was initiated a few years later.

His successor, Mr. P. L. Whytock, was manager of Eaton Hall Farm, Lady Eaton's estate at King. Lew, as he was popularly known, took a keen interest in all divisions of the show, but particularly the floriculture and dairy cattle divisions. Under his direction, Eaton Hall Farm was an active exhibitor in both divisions.

Mr. S. G. Bennett served as president in 1953 and 1954. Although a director of many companies, including Canada Packers and Dominion Stores, he is best known by those associated with the Royal as the owner of Scotsdale Farm at Georgetown, Ontario, the home of one of the outstanding Shorthorn herds on this continent.

The next president, Lt. Col. S. C. Bate was an officer in the Royal Canadian Dragoons and, for several years, was a member of Canada's equestrian team. Before becoming president, he served as chairman of the Horse Show Administrative Committee.

His successor, Mr. C. F. W. Burns, was and still is well known in business circles as a result of his association with investment and insurance companies. To the agriculturalists, however, he is known as the owner of Kingfield Farm, the home of one of Canada's leading Guernsey herds. Since serving as president of the Royal, he has had the distinction of being elected to the presidency of the Canadian Guernsey Breeders' Association.

Like his predecessor, Mr. J. H. Crang is active in the investment field and as a breeder of Guernsey cattle. In addition, the milk produced on his Glendale farm is marketed through a dairy which he operates at Newmarket, Ontario. During recent years a great many championships at the Royal have been won by animals from the Kingfield and Glendale herds.

As a young man, Mr. George Rodanz established a transport business which grew and flourished under his management. Despite the success of this enterprise, his ambition was to become a farmer. Consequently, when an attractive offer for the business was received, he accepted and bought several adjoining farms near Stouffville, Ontario which were consolidated into a unit under the name Ringwood Farms. There he maintains one of the largest Hereford herds in Ontario. Mr. Rodanz served as president of the Royal in 1961 and 1962. He is also a director of the Canadian National Exhibition.

Before becoming president in 1963, Brigadier F. C. Wallace served for several years on the Horse Show Administrative Committee, including two years as chairman. A leading Canadian industrialist, he is president of several companies and a director of a number of others. Notwithstanding his business activities he has a natural love for the land and presently lives on a farm north of Georgetown, Ontario, where he conducts a commercial sheep operation.

Col. D. B. Weldon, the 16th president of the Royal, is a director of several companies, a past chairman of the Canada Council and chairman of the Board of Governors of Western University. Despite his many interests, Prospect Farm, located a few miles north of London, Ontario, is his prized possession. There is maintains one of Canada's foremost herds of Aberdeen Angus cattle. He has been a regular exhibitor and winner of many coveted awards at the Royal.

Mr. John A. McDougald, a prominent industrialist and breeder of thoroughbred horses, had the honour of serving as president during 1967, Canada's Centennial Year. Before assuming the presidency he was a frequent exhibitor, dating back to 1930, and a member of the Horse Show Administrative and

Executive Committee. Among his many business interests Mr. McDougald is chairman of the Board of Dominion Stores Limited; chairman of the Board and president of Crown Trust, and a member of the Executive Committee of Massey Ferguson Industries Limited.

He breeds thoroughbred horses at Green Meadows, his 225 acre farm, which is located within Metropolitan Toronto. H.R.H. The Prince Philip, Duke of Edinburgh was a guest of Mr. and Mrs. McDougald during his visit to Toronto to attend the Commonwealth Society Conference and the Royal Winter Fair.

The Green Meadows Coaching Class is sponsored by Mr. McDougald and derives its name from his farm.

Because of his many activities Mr. McDougald found it necessary to break with tradition by serving as president for only one year.

At the annual meeting in March 1968, Mr. Henry Borden, Q.C., a leading Canadian lawyer and industrialist as well as a noted breeder of Guernsey cattle, was elected to succeed Mr. McDougald. Mr. Borden, who is chairman of the Board of Governors of the University of Toronto and chairman or director of a score of Canadian companies, maintains a herd of prize-winning Guernseys at his Tannery Hill Farm at King, a few miles north of Toronto. Animals exhibited by him at the 1967 Royal won all three of the centennial medals offered in the Guernsey breed competition.

It is not possible to cite the contribution that each president has made to the success of the Royal. Of primary importance is the fact that all have been dedicated to the task of building a better fair and, in the process, each has assisted in his own way in the attainment of that objective.

STAFF

Although C. F. (Bill) Bailey was the first general manager of the Royal, he never actually managed a fair. Frustrated by the delay in getting the buildings completed in time for holding a fair in 1921, and disillusioned by some of the bickering among members of the Board of Directors, he resigned early in 1922. Shortly thereafter he joined the service of the Central Experimental Farm and eventually was appointed superintendent of the Experimental Farm at Fredericton, a position he held at the time of his retirement.

Fortunately for the Association, Mr. A. P. Westervelt had been appointed assistant to Mr. Bailey in 1921 and was a logical candidate for promotion when Mr. Bailey resigned. Before joining the staff of the Royal, Mr. Westervelt held a number of positions in government service. When a live stock branch was established in the Ontario Department of Agriculture in 1906, Mr. Westervelt became the director. When responsibility for running the Ontario Provincial Winter Fair was assigned to this branch, Mr. Westervelt was named manager and gained much valuable experience in show business.

In 1914, he resigned to accept a position with the Live Stock Branch of the Federal Department of Agriculture, where he is generally credited with being responsible for establishing the market information service.

When he became general manager of the Royal, he faced many problems. The building program was not going as quickly as expected, but that problem was solved in time to hold a show in 1922. The attendance was below expectations, creating financial problems. These were solved, temporarily at least, when a new contract with the city was signed, granting the Royal more favourable terms that had been granted under the original contract, and when the federal and Ontario governments agreed to increase their annual grants to the Royal. Mr. Westervelt played a leading role in all of these negotiations and, because of this, deserves a major share of the credit for getting the fair established on a sound financial basis.

A great many changes took place during his tenure of office, and his practical and scientific knowledge of agriculture was used to promote and initiate improvements that kept the Royal abreast of the fast-changing agricultural industry.

He was always a fairly robust man, and his many friends were shocked when he suffered a cerebral hemorrhage in 1937 while sitting at his desk and died soon after.

A meeting of the directors was convened a few weeks later to appoint a successor. Although the names of several candidates were proposed, none was considered seriously except that of W. A. Dryden, the man who had served as the first president from 1919-1923 and as a member of the executive committee in the years following.

Mr. Dryden was a dynamic individual. He had definite ideas and was inclined to resent anyone who disagreed with him. Because of his positive approach he got things done, but sometimes made bad friends in the process. Few men were better known in Canada, particularly in political circles, than Bill Dryden, and no person associated with the Royal made use of his connections to better advantage in enlisting support for the Association.

While Bill Dryden was general manager from 1937 until the spring of 1949, he only managed four shows. Just as preparations for the 1939 show were being completed, World War II broke out and the buildings used by the Royal were transferred to the military authorities. Although the war ended in the summer of 1945, the buildings were not vacated by the troops in time to permit the holding of a show that year. Hence the first post-war show was delayed until 1946.

In the spring of 1948, Mr. Dryden suffered a heart seizure. Although he made a remarkable recovery, the directors were fearful that he might suffer a relapse as the pressure of managing the fair began to mount. They appealed to the Hon. T. L. Kennedy, Minister of Agriculture, for assistance. He agreed to grant the writer, who at that time was Ontario Live Stock Commissioner, leave of absence to manage the 1948 show.

In the spring of 1949, Mr. Dryden tendered his resignation on account of ill health. In the months following, his condition deterioriated rapidly and he died during the 1949 show. In the meantime, the directors had appointed Brigadier C. S. McKee as his successor. Brigadier McKee had been an active member of the Horse Show Administrative Committee for many years and had a thorough knowledge of that division of the show. Being a lawyer by profession, his knowledge of agriculture was limited. However, he proved to be an apt pupil and soon became familiar with all divisions of the show.

There were more dramatic changes in agriculture during the years that Brigadier McKee served as general manager than at any other time. He kept himself well informed on current developments and translated those developments into action, up-dating the show in keeping with the changes in the industry.

Brigadier McKee reached the age of retirement in 1963 and tendered his resignation. W. P. Watson, the writer of this book, who had just completed 35 years of service with the Ontario Department of Agriculture, as Live Stock Commissioner and Assistant Deputy Minister, was appointed to succeed him.

No general manager can hope to be successful without the enthusiastic co-operation and loyal support of a competent staff.

Those who served as general manager of the Royal were extremely fortunate in this regard. One of the first men to join the staff was Matt Aikman, who was appointed office boy in 1922 at the munificent salary of $12 per week. In the years following, he received many promotions, finally being named office manager, a position he still holds. He has the distinction of being the only member of the staff to serve throughout the Royal's history to date. Because of his intimate knowledge of the show and his vivid memory of developments of the past, he has been able to contribute a great deal of the historical information contained in this book.

Two other staff members who made their marks during the post-war period, were D. D. (Doug) Wilson and Charles Musson. Both joined the organization in 1922, Doug as Superintendent of Entries and Charles as Treasurer. Doug will be remembered by the Royal's old-timers as a strict enforcer of the rules. Late entries were returned with consummate firmness. As a result of Doug's steadfast policy, exhibitors soon learned – and, in most cases, appreciated – that the Royal was one show where rules were taken seriously.

During the war years Doug obtained a position with the National Employment Service, with responsibility for selecting personnel to man the offices which were being established under this rapidly expanding service. When the Royal staff was being re-organized after the war, Doug agreed to return out of loyalty to the Royal and at some sacrifice to himself. He retired in 1952 and died two years later.

Charles Musson, as treasurer, did not come in contact with the public to the same extent as the other employees, and was not so well known, but he was a faithful and loyal servant of the Royal.

In the re-organization which took place after the war, James R. Johnston was appointed to the staff as secretary and later on was given additional duties as assistant general manager. A diplomat in every sense, Jim has handled many knotty problems with credit to himself and to the Royal. He is particularly adept in dealing with horse show exhibitors, members of International Teams, and commercial exhibitors.

When Doug Wilson retired, J. A. (Andy) Stewart was engaged as Superintendent of Entries. His career at the Royal was short and uneventful. In 1955, he accepted an offer as manager of a large farm in South Western Ontario and has since purchased a farm in the Ailsa Craig district where he is conducting a successful corn, hog, and beef cattle operation.

He was succeeded by C. C. (Cliff) Morrow who, at the time, was a member of the staff of the Ontario Live Stock Branch. Cliff was raised on a farm in Eastern Ontario, took part in 4-H activities as a teen-ager, and graduated from the Ontario Agricultural College — all of which helped to qualify him for his duties as a supervisor of agricultural activities at the Royal.

Although these members of the staff have given excellent service to the Royal, some credit for their performances should go to the female members who worked behind the scenes. In this connection, special mention should be made of the contribution of Mrs. Edna Neill. Her efforts, particularly on behalf of the various horse show committees, has been invaluable during the post-war period.

While serving as general manager, Mr. Westervelt was fortunate in having two excellent secretaries in Miss Edith Morris and Miss Ruby McConnell. When Mr. Dryden became manager, he obtained a good deal of needed support from his secretary, Mrs. Nan Foreman.

Among those who have served the Royal faithfully and well in recent years are Mrs. Aurley Bell and Miss Mildred Boyd. All were exceedingly capable and as a result made a genuine contribution to the efficient and harmonious operations of the fair.

Although the Royal has been favoured by having an excellent permanent staff it could not have functioned efficiently without the assistance of key men in responsible positions of a temporary nature. Undoubtedly the most unforgettable character to serve in that capacity was the late J. D. (Duff) Brien. A noted Shorthorn and Berkshire breeder during the early part of the century, Duff took an active part in the preliminary organizational activities and became one of the charter members. When plans were being formalized for the first fair he accepted an invitation to become general superintendent and continued to serve until 1946.

Quite stout and jolly, Duff gave one the impression of being a playboy. Beneath his slap-happy exterior, however, he did have his serious moments. Although he seemed to have an allergy to work of any kind, he always succeeded in arranging for the work to be done. He had a phenomenal ability to quell the wrath of irate individuals and by sheer logic and native wit often succeeded in convincing them that they were the offenders rather than the persons offended.

In 1947, T. C. (Trace) Glaspell, who had been serving as sheep superintendent became the general superintendent, a position he still occupies. Like his predecessor, Trace was fairly plump and had a jolly disposition, but unlike him, he was a diligent worker. In carrying out his duties he sets the pace and expects his helpers to follow his example.

Having shown sheep at the Royal for many years, Trace has a deep appreciation of the problems of the exhibitors. This has enabled him to perform his duties in a fair and just manner to the benefit of both the exhibitors and the Royal.

LOOKING AHEAD

History is our greatest teacher and traditional patterns shape future trends. Changes in techniques are made frequently, but general principles remain fairly constant.

The founders of the Royal had one basic principle in mind, namely, that it was to be the show window of Canadian agriculture. That principle has always been a dominant factor in all planning and will always be so. Although the Royal will continue to be agriculture's show window, undoubtedly there will be many changes in the showmanship by which agriculture is presented to the public.

There will be new men at the helm and they will advance many new ideas. In the past replacements on the Executive Committee and management have been made gradually, but an accelerated rate of change is already being felt in all aspects of Canadian society. Many of those who are now guiding the destinies of the organization will, in the natural course of events, soon be replaced. This prospect does not put the future of the organization in jeopardy. Their places will be taken by younger men, with a new approach to their responsibilities, but the ultimate objects set out in the constitution will continue to guide them.

There will be a great many changes in agriculture in the next decade and the Royal will continue to reflect them. The farm population is likely to continue its downward trend. Farms will be larger, and the output per man much greater. The farmer of the future will be more interested in utility than in show-ring standards. He will be following closely the results of research and will be applying the information resulting therefrom in an effort to reduce his costs of production. Those in command will have to keep up to date on such matters, and design a program to make the Royal an important centre for the dissemination of information if they are to continue to command the support of the agricultural industry.

However the Royal cannot depend on the support of agriculturalists alone to provide the finances required to operate a show of such magnitude. In recent years the proportion of urban people attending the show has been increasing. To maintain their patronage new features must be devised to interest them. The development of a food show within the Royal appears to have the greatest possibilities for touching the common interest of farm and city people. Food links the people of both town and country, as consumers and producers.

Any further comments on the future would be in the realm of speculation. Suffice it to say that inasmuch as there have been many changes in the past there will be dramatic changes in the future. Those who have guided the destinies of the Association in the past can derive a great deal of satisfaction from the fact that the Royal has played a leading role in the development of agriculture in this country and they can look to the future, confident in the belief that it will continue to fulfill the hopes and aspirations of its founders.

Appendices and Index

BASIS OF ORGANIZATION

What makes the Royal tick? Obviously there is no single answer to that question, but its unique organizational structure must be an important factor.

Under its constitution the primary objectives of the Royal Agricultural Winter Fair are: "to establish, maintain and conduct a National Fat Stock Fair and Breeding Show in the City of Toronto for the exhibition of farm animals of all kinds, and products of the farms, dairies and apiaries, for giving prizes to exhibitors, and generally for the encouragement of Animal Husbandry and all farm industries in Canada."

To help carry out these objectives provision has been made for broad representation on the membership. Membership privileges were extended to all national live stock associations, leading provincial live stock associations, and all prominent agricultural organizations, whether national or provincial in scope. Upon being accepted to membership each association or organization may name from one to three representatives, depending on the size of its membership and the scope of its operations.

When the constitution was drafted there were relatively few large agricultural organizations in Canada but, as they evolved, they were added to the membership. Later, organizations that ceased to be active were dropped.

The member organizations are grouped into divisions for purposes of establishing committees and electing directors. For example, all member organizations interested in the breeding of horses are assigned to the breeding horse division and their representatives serve on the Breeding Horse Committee. The directors for this division are elected from among these representatives at the annual meeting of the Association. A similar procedure is followed in the other divisions of the show. As a result breed associations and agricultural organizations have a strong voice in determining the personnel of the Board of Directors.

In addition to directors elected by farm organizations, four directors are elected from among the representatives of the various Departments of Agriculture and an equal number are named to represent the horse show division. Although the term of office is one year, directors are eligible for re-election provided, of course, that they continue to represent their respective organizations.

A number of persons are members of the Board by virtue of office. Included in this category are: all Past Presidents; all Ministers and Deputy Ministers of Agriculture; the Honourary Legal Adviser, and the Chairman of the Horse Show Administrative Committee. Previous to 1968 the City of Toronto was represented by the Mayor, Chairman of the Board of Control, and the Commissioners of Parks and Recreation and of Finance. Following the transfer of the property and buildings from the City of Toronto to the Corporation of Metropolitan Toronto, City officials were replaced by Metro officials. Accordingly our new landlords are presently represented on the Board by the Chairman of the Metropolitan Council, the Mayor of Toronto, the Mayors of the five boroughs and the Metro Parks and Finance Commissioners.

Under the constitution the directors have authority to appoint eight directors at large and as many honourary directors as may be deemed advisable. The 1967 Board had a membership of 110.

Since members live in all parts of Canada, it is impractical to hold many meetings of the full Board of Directors. The Board has followed the practice of delegating responsibility for conducting the affairs of the Association to an Executive Committee. Before doing so, however, the directors elect from among their number a president and a vice-president.

The Executive Committee is made up of the president, vice-president; all past presidents; the chairman of the Horse Show Administrative Committee; the honourary legal adviser; the Chairman of the Metropolitan Toronto Council; the Commissioner of Parks for Metropolitan Toronto, and 10 persons elected from the Board of Directors.

The Executive Committee is primarily concerned with fiscal matters and with the development of special features in the show. Each year management drafts a budget under the guidance of a budget chief. When it is approved by the Executive Committee every division is expected to operate within the amount budgeted.

Naturally the members of the Executive Committee are interested in all phases of the show. For obvious reasons, however, they cannot be expected to master the details of every division. Consequently committees have been established for each division. Generally speaking, the representatives of the member associations constitute the majority of the membership on these committees but, quite frequently, men prominent in the particular field of activity, are added. The chairman and vice-chairman of each committee are named by the Executive Committee.

Each committee meets during the spring months to formulate a program for its division. Classifications, prize offerings and rules are methodically reviewed. In arriving at decisions the recommendations of member associations are carefully considered. Generally speaking, their recommendations with respect to the appointment of judges are accepted. However the Executive Committee reserves the right to be the final arbiter in such matters.

Any show of the magnitude of the Royal must have a permanent staff. At the time of the first fair the staff was comprised of a general manager, a treasurer, a superintendent of entries, and a number of secretarial and clerical assistants. As the fair expanded the staff was increased, some of the titles were changed but basically the responsibilities of each member has remained the same.

Under the constitution, the general manager and senior assistants are appointed by the Board of Directors, usually on the recommendation of the Executive Committee. They are responsible for co-ordinating the activities of the various committees, executing the decisions of the Executive Committee and generally for supervising the operations of the fair.

Although the term of office of president is not specified in the constitution, it has become traditional for presidents to serve for two years. Another tradition which has been observed is that of alternating the presidency between men whose main interest is either the horse show or agriculture. Thus, when the president is a representative of the horse show division, the vice-president is elected from the agricultural division and vice-versa.

Undoubtedly a great deal of the success of the Royal stems from the wisdom that was displayed in establishing the basis of organization. Basically it is organized from the bottom up rather than from the top down. By including in membership representatives of government, of all agricultural organizations that have attained a recognized status and of horse show enthusiasts, the Royal has enlisted the support and co-operation of individuals and groups which are primarily interested in promoting the welfare of Canada's basic industry. These representatives have an excellent opportunity of displaying their talents at the committee meetings where frankness is the general rule rather than the exception. The members of the Executive Committee have always displayed a wholesome respect for the opinions of the committee members, and support their recommendations provided, of course, that they can be implemented within the budget.

GRAND CHAMPION STEER

YEAR	EXHIBITOR	ADDRESS	BREED	SELLING PRICE	BUYER
1922	E. T. Howse & Son	Ariss, Ont.	Hereford		
1923	Ray Clarkson	Weston, Ont.	Shorthorn	$ 1.55	
1924	J. M. Gardhouse	Weston, Ont.	Shorthorn	$ 1.60	
1925	J. M. Gardhouse	Weston, Ont.	Shorthorn	$ 1.55	
1926	University of Alberta	Edmonton, Alta.	Shorthorn	—	
1927	University of Alberta	Edmonton, Alta.	Shorthorn	$ 1.65	
1928	Briarcliff Farms	Pine Plains, N.Y.	A. Angus	$ 1.81	
1929	E. Robson & Sons	Denfield, Ont.	Shorthorn	$ 1.25	
1930	F. H. Deacon	Unionville, Ont.	Shorthorn	$ 1.00	
1931	University of Alberta	Edmonton, Alta.	A. Angus	$ .50	
1932	University of Alberta	Edmonton, Alta.	A. Angus	—	
1933	J. A. McAllister	Guelph, Ont.	A. Angus	—	
1934	E. S. McDonald	Brookdale, Man.	A. Angus	$ .60	
1935	McKenzie Hall	Ayr, Ont.	Shorthorn	$ .75	
1936	University of Alberta	Edmonton, Alta.	Shorthorn	$ .75	
1937	University of Alberta	Edmonton, Alta.	Shorthorn	$ .50	
1938	University of Alberta	Edmonton, Alta.	Shorthorn	$ .40	
1946	F. W. Reicheld & Son	Jarvis, Ont.	Hereford	$13.00	T. Eaton Co. Ltd.
1947	Lloyd Mack	Rockwood, Ont.	A. Angus	$ 9.50	T. Eaton Co. Ltd.
1948	Lloyd Mack	Rockwood, Ont.	A. Angus	$ 6.00	T. Eaton Co. Ltd.
1949	Ed. F. Noad	Claresholm, Alta.	Shorthorn	$ 2.40	Loblaw Groceterias Co. Ltd.
1950	University of Alberta	Edmonton, Ont.	Shorthorn	$ 1.40	Chas. Hemstead
1951	University of Alberta	Edmonton, Ont.	Shorthorn	$ 2.30	T. Eaton Co. Ltd.
1952	Carr Hatch	Unionville, Ont.	A. Angus	$ 2.25	Club One Two
1953	Ed. F. Noad	Claresholm, Alta.	Shorthorn	$ 2.50	Loblaw Groceterias Co. Ltd.
1954	Carr Hatch	Unionville, Ont.	A. Angus	$ 1.85	Club One Two
1955	Ed. F. Noad	Claresholm, Alta.	Hereford	$ 2.60	Loblaw Groceterias Co. Ltd.

1956	Edwards Bros.	Watford, Ont.	A. Angus	$ 1.75	Loblaw Groceterias Co. Ltd.
1957	Ross M. Kohler & Son	Cayuga, Ont.	A. Angus	$ 2.00	Loblaw Groceterias Co. Ltd.
1958	A. R. Cross	Midnapore, Alta.	Shorthorn	$ 2.00	Loblaw Groceterias Co. Ltd.
1959	McIntyre Ranching Co.	Lethbridge, Alta.	Hereford	$ 2.30	Loblaw Groceterias Co. Ltd.
1960	Leo Halstead	Carbon, Alta.	Shorthorn	$10.00	Dominion Stores Ltd.
1961	Leo Halstead	Carbon, Alta.	Shorthorn	$11.00	Dominion Stores Ltd.
1962	Marion & Don Johnson	Burrows, Sask.	Hereford	$12.50	Dominion Stores Ltd.
1963	Angus Glen Farms Ltd. and Marvin Hinton	Unionville, Ont. Mount Sterling, Ohio	A. Angus	$11.75	Dominion Stores Ltd.
1964	Meadow Lane Farm	North Salem, N.Y. and King, Ontario	A. Angus	$11.00	Dominion Stores Ltd.
1965	Boyd P. Brown	King, Ontario and North Salem, N.Y.	A. Angus	$13.00	Dominion Stores Ltd.
1966	Desourdy Construction Ltd.	West Shefford, Que.	A. Angus	$13.25	Dominion Stores Ltd.
1967	Windfield Farms Ltd.	Willowdale, Ont.	A. Angus	$10.25	Dominion Stores Ltd.

N.B. *Names of the buyers during 1922-38 not available.*

YEAR	NAME	ADDRESS	SELLING PRICE	BREED
1946	John Kinsman	Cromarty	$ 5.50	Shorthorn
1947	Kenneth McKinnon	Hillsburg	$10.50	Angus
1948	Kenneth McKinnon	Hillsburg	$ 3.00	Angus
1949	Duncan Campbell	Moffat	$ 2.00	Shorthorn
1950	Alex McIntosh	Guelph	$ 2.00	Angus
1951	Robert Hern	Granton	$ 2.05	Hereford
1952	William Dunbar	Guelph	$ 2.00	Hereford
1953	Ross Graham	Palmerston	$ 2.25	Angus
1954	Katharine Merry	Oakville	$ 1.60	Shorthorn
1955	Murray Gaunt	Wingham	$ 2.50	Shorthorn
1956	Donald Pullen	Granton	$ 1.75	Angus
1957	Helen Anderson	Glen Cross	$ 1.95	Shorthorn
1958	James Wettlaufer	Baden	$ 2.00	Angus
1959	George Earley	Kerwood	$ 2.20	Angus
1960	John Giles	Glencoe	$ 4.75	Angus
1961	Shirley Earley	Kerwood	$ 7.00	Angus
1962	Ronald Storey	Guelph	$ 9.00	Angus
1963	Sandra Peart	Guelph	$ 8.25	Shorthorn
1964	Boyd Nelson	Codrington	$ 8.50	Angus
1965	Bert Tupling	Honeywood	$ 8.50	Hereford
1966	David Hasson	Ariss	$ 9.25	Angus
1967	Bill Lasby	Rockwood	$ 9.00	Shorthorn

CHAIRMEN

HORSE SHOW ADMINISTRATIVE COMMITTEE

1922 - 1967

1922-24	Lt. Colonel Herbert C. Cox
1925-29	Mr. Alfred Rogers
1930-32	Major Clifford Sifton
1933-37	Mr. Gordon F. Perry
1938	Mr. John W. McKee
1946-47	Mr. F. K. Morrow
1948-49	Major-General C. C. Mann, C.B.E., D.S.Q.
1950-54	Lt. Colonel Stuart C. Bate, O.B.E.
1955-56	Mr. Harold Crang
1957-58	Mr. Trumbull Warren, O.B.E.
1959-60	Brigadier F. C. Wallace, D.S.O., M.C., M.F.H.
1961-63	Lt. Colonel Charles Baker
1964-65	Mr. W. A. Harris
1966-67	Lt. Colonel Charles Baker

STAKE DONORS

The following are persons who contributed
prize money in stake classes in the Horse Show:

Mr. C. F. W. Burns

Lt. Col. G. Allan Burton, D.S.O., E.D., M.F.H.

Mr. C. L. Burton, C.B.E.

Hon. G. P. Campbell, Q.C., LL.D.

Mr. J. H. Crang

Mr. Norman J. Dawes

Mr. Moffat Dunlap

Mr. D. C. Durland

Col. R. Y. Eaton

Mr. A. L. Ellsworth

Mr. J. W. Horsey

Mr. John Irwin

Mr. John A. McDougald

Col. Harry McGee

Mr. John W. McKee

Col. R. S. McLaughlin

Mr. J. Y. Murdock

Sir Harry Oakes

Mr. Gordon F. Perry

Lt. Col. W. E. Phillips, C.B.E., D.S.O., M.C.

Mrs. Eric Phillips

Mr. Alfred Rogers

Mr. Arthur Schmon

Mr. Robert Schmon

Sir Clifford Sifton

Mr. J. E. Smallman

Mr. C. O. Stillman

Mr. E. P. Taylor, C.M.G.

Brig. F. C. Wallace, D.S.O., M.E., M.F.H.

Mr. E. R. Wood

In addition, stakes were donated by the Royal York Hotel
during the years 1929-38, and by the presidents of the
Canadian Pacific Railway, during the years 1946-67.

G. HOWARD FERGUSON TROPHY

In 1925, Hon. G. Howard Ferguson, Premier of Ontario, donated the trophy which bears his name, to be awarded to the winning team in International Jumping Competition. This trophy has been won by teams representing the following countries:

1925	Belgium	1950	United States
1926	France	1951	Eire
1927	no competition	1952	France
1928	United States	1953	England
1929	no competition	1954	Spain
1930	United States	1955	Eire
1931	Irish Free State	1956	United States
1932	Canada	1957	United States
1933	Irish Free State	1958	Germany
1934	United States	1959	United States
1935	Irish Free State	1960	United States
1936	Canada	1961	United States
1937	Holland	1962	United States
1938	Eire	1963	Germany
1946	Mexico	1964	United States
1947	United States	1965	United States
1948	France	1966	Canada
1949	Mexico	1967	United States

Members of Canadian
teams participating in
International Competition:

In the 1920's	Capt. Stuart C. Bate
	Lt. G. F. Elliott
	Capt. L. D. Hammond
	Major R. S. Timmis
In the 1930's	Lt. A. P. Ardagh
	Capt. Stuart C. Bate
	Lt. E. W. H. Berwick
	Lt. P. C. R. Black
	Lt. Douglas Cleland
	Lt. Marshall Cleland
	Col. L. D. Hammond
	Lt. D. Hunter
	Lt. H. A. Phillips
	Lt. Col. W. L. Rawlinson
	Col. R. S. Timmis
In the 1940's	Major Charles Baker, Jr.
	Lt. W. R. Ballard
	Squadron Leader Douglas Cleland
	Major Gordon Gayford
	2nd Lt. Thomas Gayford
	Major J. H. Larocque
	Lt. Col. H. A. Phillips
In the 1950's	Lt. Col. Chas. Baker
	Lt. W. R. Ballard
	Mr. Douglas Cudney
	Mr. James Elder
	Mr. Thomas Gayford
	Mr. Douglas Hood
	Maj. Gen. C. C. Mann
	Mr. L. J. McGuinness
	Capt. Colm O'Shea
	Miss Shirley Thomas
In the 1960's	Lt. Col. Charles Baker
	Mr. Douglas Cudney
	Mr. James Day
	Mr. Moffat Dunlap
	Mr. James Elder
	Mr. Thomas Gayford
	Miss Gail Ross
	Mr. Melvin Stone

EARLY LIVE STOCK EXHIBITORS

Prominent live stock exhibitors
at the first three Royals (1922-24):

Breeding Horses

CLYDESDALES	Mr. W. F. Batty	Brooklin, Ont.
	Brandon Bros.	Forest, Ont.
	Graham Bros.	Claremont, Ont.
	Albert Hewson	Malton, Ont.
	R. R. Ness & Sons	Howick, Que.
	Ben Rothwell	Ottawa, Ont.
	Smith & Richardson	Columbus, Ont.
	James Torrance	Markham, Ont.
PERCHERONS	J. E. Arnold & Son	Grenville, Que.
	Geo. T. Fraser	Tate, Sask.
	Chas. Head	Regina, Sask.
	W. E. Morden	Oakville, Ont.
	Archie Pedden	Strathroy, Ont.
BELGIANS	C. W. Gurney	Paris, Ont.
	D. V. Runkle	Regina, Sask.
	Robert Thomas	Grandora, Sask.
STANDARD BREDS	Crow & Murray	Toronto, Ont.
	Cruickston Stock Farm	Galt, Ont.
	G. A. M. Davidson	Unionville, Ont.
THOROUGHBREDS	Canadian Racing Association	Toronto, Ont.
	Thorncliffe Stable	Toronto, Ont.
HACKNEYS	Thos. F. Barnet	Renfrew, Ont.
	Crow & Murray	Toronto, Ont.
	Robt. Kerr	Acton, Ont.
	Joseph Telfer	Milton West, Ont.
	James Tilt	Brampton, Ont.
PONIES	Dr. W. J. R. Fowler	Guelph, Ont.
	G. W. Lucas	Toronto, Ont.
	John Pringle	London, Ont.
	A. Yeager	Simcoe, Ont.

Beef Cattle

SHORTHORNS	Campbell & Amos	Moffat, Ont.
	Carpenter & Ross	Mansfield, Ohio
	Col. F. H. Deacon	Unionville, Ont.
	James Douglas & Sons	Caledonia, Ont.
	W. A. Dryden	Brooklin, Ont.
	John Gardhouse & Sons	Weston, Ont.
	Maryvale Farms	Youngstown, Ohio
	Harry McGee	Islington, Ont.
	John Miller, Jr.	Ashburn, Ont.
	T. A. Russell	Downsview, Ont.
	J. A. Watt	Elora, Ont.
DUAL PURPOSE SHORTHORNS	The Donald Woodward Herd	LeRoy, N.Y.
	Wm. E. & Harry Hewitt	York, Ont.
	Alexander MacLaren	Buckingham, Que.
	Ross Martindale	Caledonia, Ont.
	Peart Bros.	Caledonia, Ont.
	G. L. Smith	Meadowvale, Ont.
HEREFORDS	W. H. Black	Caledon, Ont.
	O. A. Boggs & Sons	Daysland, Alta.
	L. O. Clifford	Oshawa, Ont.
	G. F. Collicut	Crossfield, Alta.
	A. A. Macdonald	Kirkfield, Ont.
	W. T. McCray	Kentland, Indiana
	McNeil & McNeil	Dutton, Ont.
	N. E. Parish	Reading, Pa.
	Walter Readhead	Milton, Ont.
	Shadeland Farm	Lafayette, Ind.
ABERDEEN ANGUS	James Bowman	Guelph, Ont.
	G. C. Channon	Oakwood, Ont.
	John D. Larkin	Queenston, Ont.
	George McAllister & Son Ltd.	Guelph, Ont.
	James D. McGregor	Brandon, Man.
	Woodcote Stock Farm	Ionia, Mich.

Dairy Cattle

HOLSTEINS	Dickie Bros.	Truro, N.S.
	Dyment Bros.	Dundas, Ont.
	Haley & Lee	Springford, Ont.
	John Harvey	Frelighsburg, Que.
	Hilliker Bros.	Norwich, Ont.
	A. E. Hulet	Norwich, Ont.
	J. W. Innes	Woodstock, Ont.
	Rettie Bros.	Norwich, Ont.
	Walburn Rivers	Ingersoll, Ont.
AYRSHIRES	Alta Crest Farms	Spencer, Mass
	E. J. Davis	Meadowvale, Ont.
	H. C. Hamel & Sons	Markham, Ont.
	Gilbert McMillan	Huntingdon, Que.
	H. McPherson	Norwich, Ont.
	A. McRae & Sons	Charlottetown, P.E.I.
	R. R. Ness & Sons	Howick, Que.
	Geo. Pearson & Sons	Waterdown, Ont.
	W. C. Wylie	Howick, Que.
JERSEYS	James Bagg & Sons	Edgeley, Ont.
	B. H. Bull & Sons	Brampton, Ont.
	R. J. Fleming	Toronto, Ont.
	A. T. Little	London, Ont.
	Papple Bros.	Brantford, Ont.
	John Pringle	London, Ont.
	Richmond Jersey Inc.	Richmond, Que.
GUERNSEYS	Howard W. Corning	Chegoggin, N.S.
	D. A. Dunlap	Todmorden, Ont.
	Martindale Farms	St. Catharines, Ont.
	D. G. McKay & Son	Scotsburn, N.S.
	J. Milligan & Son	Westville, N.S.
	Roper Bros.	Charlottetown, P.E.I.
	Roselawn Farms	Roches Point, Ont.
	J. A. Telfer	Paris, Ont.
FRENCH CANADIANS	Arsene Denis	St. Norbert, Que.
	Albina Sylvestre	St. Simon de Bagot, Que.

Sheep

Peter Arkell & Sons	Teeswater, Ont.
A. Ayre	Hampton, Ont.
David D. Bell & Son	Shakespeare, Ont.
E. Brien & Sons	Ridgetown, Ont.
James A. Campbell	Thedford, Ont.
Fillmore Farms	Old Bennington, Vt.
W. Glaspell & Sons	Oshawa, Ont.
F. W. Gurney	Paris, Ont.
J. P. Henderson & Son	Guelph, Ont.
John R. Kelsey	Woodville, Ont.
John D. Larkin	Queenston, Ont.
H. M. Lee	Highate, Ont.
G. H. Mark & Son	Little Britain, Ont.
Robert McEwen	London, Ont.
John Packham & Sons	Caistor Centre, Ont.
R. S. Robson & Son	Denfield, Ont.
Chas. J. Shore	Glanworth, Ont.
Levi Skinner & Son	Tyrone, Ont.
James Snell & Sons	Clinton, Ont.
J. W. Springstead & Sons	Caistor Centre, Ont.
Cecil Stobbs	Wheatley, Ont.
Telfer Bros.	Paris, Ont.
A. & W. Whitelaw	Guelph, Ont.
Robert Young	Glanford, Ont.

Swine

J. E. Brethour and Nephew	Burford, Ont.
E. Brien & Sons	Ridgetown, Ont.
W. W. Brownridge	Georgetown, Ont.
Henry Copes	Wyoming, Ont.
D. Douglas & Sons	Mitchell, Ont.
Alex Dynes	Ottawa, Ont.
J. K. Featherston	Streetsville, Ont.
George C. Gould	Essex, Ont.
James C. Hart	Gadshill, Ont.
J. Lerch & Sons	Preston, Ont.
P. J. McEwen	Wyoming, Ont.
G. W. Miners	Exeter, Ont.
R. R. Rudd & Son	Guelph, Ont.
W. E. Wright & Son	Glanworth, Ont.

During its first 39 years of operations the Royal was honoured in having the following distinguished persons officiate at the opening ceremonies.

1922	His Honour, Col. Henry Cockshutt, Lieutenant Governor, Province of Ontario.
1923	Hon. G. Howard Ferguson, Premier, Province of Ontario.
1924	His Honour, Mr. Narcisse Perodeau, Lieutenant Governor of Quebec.
1925	Hon. G. Howard Ferguson, Premier, Province of Ontario.
1926	His Honour, Col. Henry Cockshutt, Lieutenant Governor, Province of Ontario.
1927	His Excellency, the Viscount Willingdon, Governor-General of Canada.
1928	Right. Hon. W. L. Mackenzie King, Prime Minister of Canada.
1929	His Honour, Mr. W. D. Ross, Lieutenant Governor, Province of Ontario.
1930	Right Hon. Sir Robert Borden, Prime Minister of Canada.
1931	His Honour, Mr. W. D. Ross, Lieutenant Governor, Province of Ontario.
1932	Right Hon. R. B. Bennett, Prime Minister of Canada.
1933	Hon. E. N. Rhodes, Minister of Finance for Canada.
1934	Hon. Mitchell F. Hepburn, Premier, Province of Ontario.
1935	Hon. Harry C. Nixon, Provincial Secretary, Province of Ontario.
1936	Hon. James G. Gardiner, Minister of Agriculture for Canada.
1937	Hon. Norman Armour, United States Minister to Canada.
1938	Hon. Maurice Duplessis, Premier, Province of Quebec.
1946	His Excellency, Hon. Ray Atherton, United States Ambassador to Canada.
1947	Right Hon. Louis S. St. Laurent, Secretary of State for External Affairs for Canada.
1948	Hon. T. L. Kennedy, Premier, Province of Ontario.
1949	Right Hon. Lester B. Pearson, Secretary of State for External Affairs for Canada.

1950   Right Hon. Lord Beaverbrook.

1951   Right Hon. C. D. Howe, Minister of Trade and Commerce for Canada.

1952   Gen. Sir Archibald Nye, United Kingdom High Commissioner at Ottawa.

1953   Hon. F. S. Thomas, Minister of Agriculture for Ontario.

1954   Field Marshal, the Viscount Montgomery of Alemein.

1955   His Excellency, Sir Roger Makins, British Ambassador to United States.

1956   Hon. W. A. Goodfellow, Minister of Agriculture for Ontario.

1957   Right Hon. John G. Diefenbaker, Prime Minister of Canada.

1958   His Excellency, Right Hon. Vincent Massey, Governor-General of Canada.

1959   His Grace, Duke of Northumberland.

1960   Hon. Leslie M. Frost, Premier, Province of Ontario.

1961   Right Hon. the Earl of Feversham.

1962   Mr. Arthur Godfrey.

1963   His Worship, Donald D. Summerville, Mayor, City of Toronto.

1964   Hon. John Robarts, Premier, Province of Ontario.

1965   Mr. William R. Allen, Q.C., Chairman of the Council for the Municipality of Metropolitan Toronto.

1966   Right Hon. the Earl Beatty.

1967   H.R.H. Prince Philip, Duke of Edinburgh.

ACKNOWLEDGEMENTS

We wish to acknowledge the following known sources of photographs used in
this book: Canada Pictures, Turofsky, Canadian Army, Budd, Alexandra
Studio, Strohmeyer & Carpenter, Toronto Star, Jones & Morris, Rice & Bell.